NEW MEXICO ROCKS!

A Guide to Geologic Sites in the Land of Enchantment

NATHALIE BRANDES

PHOTOGRAPHS BY **PAUL BRANDES**

2021

Mountain Press Publishing Company

Missoula, Montana

To Ronald Derrick, my father.
You started me on this epic journey.

To Paul, my husband.
The best field partner I could ask for in the adventures of life.

GEOLOGY ROCKS!

A state-by-state series that introduces readers to some of the
most compelling and accessible geologic sites in each state.

Photographs by Paul Brandes unless otherwise credited.

Illustrations constructed by Chelsea M. Feeney
(www.cmcfeeney.com)

Front cover photo: *Navajo Church (Church Rock) is a colorful landmark sculpted from rocks of the Morrison Formation.*

Back cover photo: *Looking north down the axis of the Tierra Amarilla anticline. The white rocks forming the top of the cliffs are the Todilto Formation. The mounds in the center of the eroded anticline are travertine deposits created by springs.*

Library of Congress Cataloging-in-Publication Data

Names: Brandes, Nathalie, 1975- author. | Brandes, Paul, 1974- illustrator.
 Title: New Mexico rocks! : a guide to geologic sites in the Land of
 Enchantment / Nathalie Brandes ; photographs by Paul Brandes.
Other titles: Geology rocks! (Mountain Press Publishing Company)
Description: Missoula, Montana : Mountain Press Publishing Company, 2021. |
 Series: Geology rocks! | Includes bibliographical references and index.
 | Summary: "To discover geologic novelties in the Land of Enchantment,
 all that is required is a good map, a sense of adventure, and New Mexico
 Rocks, a guide to 60 of the most compelling geologic sites in the state.
 —Provided by publisher.
Identifiers: LCCN 2021025185 | ISBN 9780878427048 (paperback)
Subjects: LCSH: Geology—New Mexico—Guidebooks. | Rocks—New Mexico. |
 LCGFT: Guidebooks.
Classification: LCC QE143 .B736 2021 | DDC 557.89—dc23

PRINTED IN THE UNITED STATES

Mountain Press
PUBLISHING COMPANY
P.O. Box 2399 • Missoula, MT 59806 • 406-728-1900
800-234-5308 • info@mtnpress.com
www.mountain-press.com

ACKNOWLEDGMENTS

A book like this is impossible to write without the help and support of many friends and colleagues. First, I must thank my parents. They provided invaluable support in pursuing my career in geology. Special thanks to my father, who opened the world of geology to me with my first geology lessons. I still remember learning about thrust faults when I was four years old. I am also indebted to the faculty and staff of the Earth and Environmental Sciences Department at New Mexico Tech and the New Mexico Bureau of Geology and Mineral Resources. They have always been ready to help, and whenever I return to Socorro, I feel like I'm home. My gratitude also extends to the mindat.org community whose members have been very helpful with requests for photos and information. Lastly, special thanks to my husband, Paul, who trekked across New Mexico with me, read and edited drafts of this manuscript, and provided most of the photographs.

Special thanks to everyone who provided photographs.
Frank Karasti: Rio Grande Gorge (site 21), Lake Valley chlorargyrite (site 49), and Chino open pit (site 47).
Larry Maltby: Rio Grande Gorge Bridge (site 21), speleothems in Carlsbad Caverns (site 60).
Kelsey McNamara: Columnar joints at Cabezon Peak (site 5).
Marli Miller: Mora hogbacks (site 13).
Don Saathoff: Minerals from Chloride (site 43).
Tama Higuchi: *Dimetrodon* illustration (site 38).
Rob Lavinsky: Apache tear (site 20).
All other photographs were provided by Paul Brandes.

PREFACE

New Mexico, the Land of Enchantment, is the fifth largest state in the United States. This substantial area includes tall mountains, vast deserts, deep canyons, sand dunes, forests, and grasslands. These beautiful areas have their share of hazards, such as steep loose rocks, cliffs, rattlesnakes, and other wildlife, so be careful when visiting. Tell someone about your travel plans, and bring a good map, food, and plenty of water. Be prepared for whatever the day's weather will be—sizzling temperatures, thunderstorms, and blowing sand are just some of the possibilities—and remember that the weather can change quickly.

The majority of the sites in this book can be reached with a passenger car on paved roads. Exceptions to this are sites 3, 4, 8, 9, 15, 16, 23, 24, 27, 29, 30, 39, 40, 42, 44, 52, and 59, which are accessed via gravel and/or dirt roads. It is advisable to check road conditions before visiting these sites.

The sixty locations described in this book include national parks and monuments, state parks and monuments, public lands, private property, and Native American reservations. Collecting rocks and minerals is prohibited in some areas, and permits are required for others. Make sure to follow all applicable laws and be respectful of property rights. It is my hope the reader not only enjoys the beauty of the Land of Enchantment, but also learns a little about the fascinating natural processes that have shaped the state.

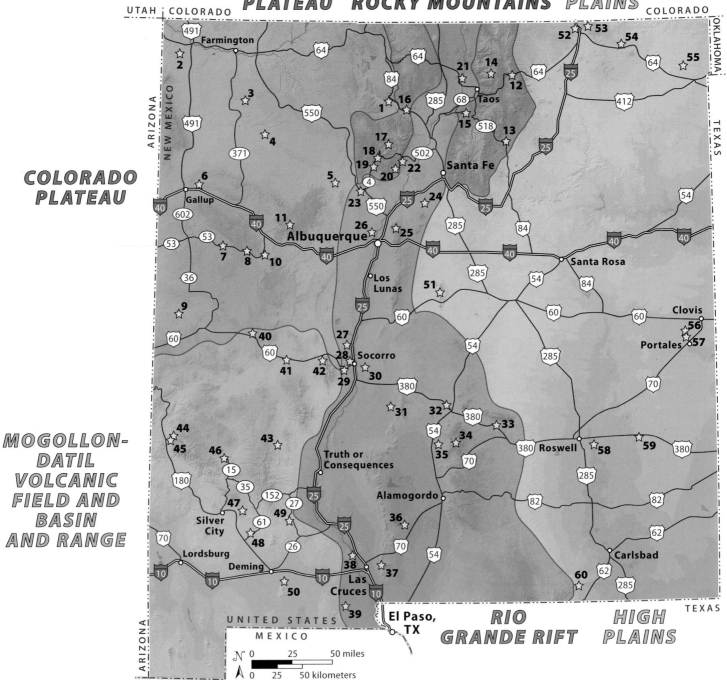

CONTENTS

GEOLOGIC TIME SCALE

ERA	PERIOD		AGE (millions of years)	GEOLOGIC EVENTS IN NEW MEXICO
CENOZOIC	Quaternary			mountain glaciers recent volcanism in Jemez Mountains and other areas
CENOZOIC			2.6	
CENOZOIC	Tertiary			Rio Grande Rift forms Mogollon-Datil volcanism Basin and Range extension in southern New Mexico
			66	
MESOZOIC	Cretaceous			Western Interior Seaway Laramide orogeny extinction of dinosaurs
MESOZOIC			145	
MESOZOIC	Jurassic			windblown and evaporite deposits in an arid climate
MESOZOIC			201	
MESOZOIC	Triassic			terrestrial, floodplain, delta, and coastal deposits dinosaurs appear
			252	
PALEOZOIC	Permian			reef complex in southern New Mexico evaporites deposited in arid climate
PALEOZOIC			299	
PALEOZOIC	Carboniferous	Pennsylvanian		assembly of supercontinent Pangea Ancestral Rocky Mountains form shallow sea covers parts of New Mexico
PALEOZOIC	Carboniferous		323	
PALEOZOIC	Carboniferous	Mississippian		
PALEOZOIC			359	
PALEOZOIC	Devonian			
PALEOZOIC			419	episodes of sea level rise and fall
PALEOZOIC	Silurian			invertebrate organisms and fish abundant in warm shallow seas
PALEOZOIC			444	
PALEOZOIC	Ordovician			
PALEOZOIC			485	
PALEOZOIC	Cambrian			
			541	
PROTEROZOIC EON				Proterozoic ends with breakup of Rodinia and a long period of erosion mountain building episodes sedimentation New Mexico part of supercontinent Rodinia oldest rocks in New Mexico (1,750 million years old) form accretion of Yavapai Province (1,800–1,700 million years ago) and Mazatzal Province (1,700–1,600 million years ago) to Laurentia
PROTEROZOIC EON			2,500	
ARCHEAN EON				
ARCHEAN EON			4,000	
HADEAN EON				
HADEAN EON			4,600	approximate age of Earth

A BRIEF HISTORY OF NEW MEXICO GEOLOGY

Earth is about 4.6 billion years old. Over this vast abyss of time, many events have shaped the planet. Continents have moved around Earth's surface in the slow dance called plate tectonics. Sea level has risen and fallen, sometimes flooding substantial areas of the continents under seawater. After several billion years of evolution, plants and animals began to inhabit the seas. When they died and sank to the bottom, they were preserved as fossils in the accumulating sediment. On land, wind, water, and ice relentlessly sculpted the surface, grinding mountains down to plains, only to have tectonic movement create new mountains. At this point in geologic time, New Mexico has mountains, plains, and much more; it's a geologically diverse state with beautiful landscapes and fascinating rocks.

Earth's earliest history, a time called the Hadean, was inhospitable to life. A thin crust of solid rock had barely cooled from liquid magma, while meteorites bombarded the surface. Over time, water condensed, and the first oceans formed. Very few rocks from this time are preserved on Earth. None have been found in New Mexico.

During the next period of geologic history, the Archean Eon, the first life appeared on Earth in the form of simple single-celled organisms. Early continents also appeared at this time, and plate tectonics, one of the most important processes to shape the planet, revved into gear. Plates are pieces of Earth's outer shell (the lithosphere) that move around slowly. While this movement is practically imperceptible, only a few centimeters every year, over time this subtle movement has profound impacts. The plates are made of two basic types of crust—continental and oceanic. Continental crust is less dense and relatively thick, while oceanic crust is denser and less thick. Thus, when the two types of crust push against each other, the thinner and denser ocean crust sinks under the continental crust in a process called subduction. By the end of the Archean, about 2.5 billion years

ago, the small continent known as Laurentia had formed, and it would eventually grow into North America. At this time, however, it did not yet include New Mexico.

The oldest rocks in New Mexico are 1.75 billion years old, from Proterozoic time, when a subduction zone existed along the southern margin of Laurentia. As the ocean plate to its south moved north and sank beneath the continent, the plate carried small microcontinents, island arcs, and other bodies of rock to the edge of the continent. Known as terranes, these rock masses were too thick and not dense enough to subduct, so they crashed into Laurentia and became sutured to the continent in a mountain building event known as an orogeny. Over time, the addition of each successive terrane increased Laurentia's quantity of basement rocks—the intrusive igneous and metamorphic rocks that form the foundation of continents. Basement rocks exist everywhere but are often hidden under younger sedimentary rocks.

New Mexico's oldest rocks are part of the Yavapai Province, a volcanic island arc terrane similar to Japan that collided with Laurentia 1.8 to 1.7 billion years ago. Another volcanic terrane, the Mazatzal Province, was added to Laurentia 1.7 to 1.6 billion years ago. The suture zone where these two provinces meet is marked by the Jemez lineament, a prominent zone of crustal weakness along which significant recent volcanism has occurred. Exposures of these basement rocks are limited to parts of the Sangre de Cristo Mountains, the Sierra Nacimiento, and the Zuni Mountains.

The growth of Laurentia continued through the Proterozoic Eon as the Granite-Rhyolite Province was added between 1.5 and 1.35 billion years ago. The exact history of these intrusive igneous and volcanic rocks is still debated. They form the basement of a small part of southeastern New Mexico and extend east through Oklahoma to Missouri and Arkansas.

By the late Proterozoic, all continents were assembled as a supercontinent known as Rodinia. In North America, collisions that helped build Rodinia are collectively called the Grenville orogeny. Rocks of this major mountain building event exist from northeast Canada south into Texas and terminate just to the southeast of New Mexico. By the end of the Proterozoic, this supercontinent was breaking apart.

The Phanerozoic Eon, the most recent 541 million years, has been marked by transgressions and regressions, which are periods of rising and falling global sea level. Of the six major transgressions, all but the most recent affected New Mexico, sometimes flooding much of the state. Multicellular life, which first appeared in the Proterozoic, diversified in the Phanerozoic and evolved into the myriad plants and animals that occupy the many unique ecosystems of Earth.

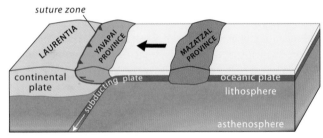

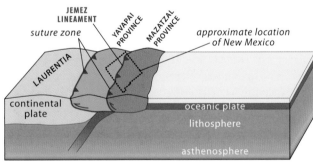

Laurentia, the continent that would become North America, grew larger during the Proterozoic Eon as terranes were added. This continental growth can be seen in the basement rocks of New Mexico, which consist primarily of the Yavapai and Mazatzal Provinces. The Jemez lineament, a zone of crustal weakness, marks where these two provinces were joined.

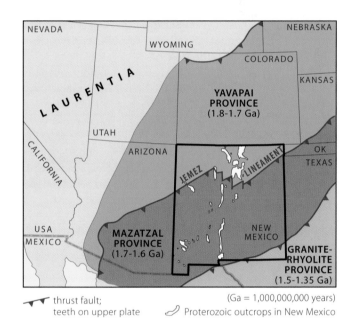

The basement rocks form the foundation of the continent. The different provinces, composed of terranes, show how the early continent grew over time.

The first major sea level rise, known as the Sauk transgression, occurred during the Cambrian Period. At this time New Mexico was located near the equator along a passive margin of Laurentia. A passive margin is not a plate boundary but rather a coastal area, similar to the modern Atlantic shore of the United States, where the sea covers the continental shelf and there is no subduction zone or plate collision. By Cambrian time, Laurentia had been exposed to almost half a billion years of weathering and erosion. No plant or animal life occupied the land then, but marine life, such as algae and early invertebrates like trilobites, existed in the seas. As sea level rose it submerged a barren landscape of rock and sandy sediment. The shoreline moved eastward and northward across New Mexico, and the sea eventually covered almost all of Laurentia except a higher region, called the Transcontinental Arch, that cut across the center of the continent. Sandstone and limestone deposited in this sea are found in the southern part of New Mexico.

In the early Ordovician the sea level dropped, resulting in a period of erosion before rising again in what is called the Tippecanoe transgression that lasted into the Silurian Period. Sea level was even higher than the previous transgression. Sitting between the equator and 30 degrees south latitude, this warm sea was home to abundant life. By the end of the Silurian, sea level began falling.

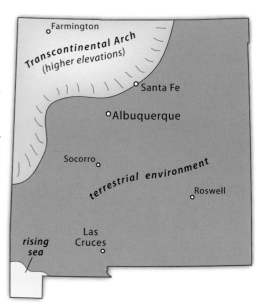

At the beginning of the Cambrian, most of the state, including the higher elevations of the Transcontinental Arch, was above sea level and undergoing erosion.

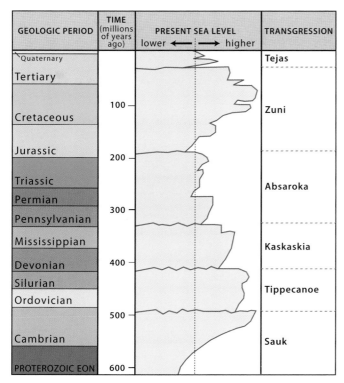

Six major transgressions (times of high global sea level) have occurred over the past 600 million years. New Mexico was affected by all but the most recent of these (the Tejas).

Only parts of south and western New Mexico were covered by seawater during the Kaskaskia transgression during the Devonian Period. Most of the state was above sea level and undergoing erosion. Also at this time, Laurentia joined together with northern Europe, creating a large continent known as Euramerica (or Laurussia). New Mexico sat at the southwest edge of this continent about 20 to 30 degrees south of the equator. Sea level continued to rise into the Mississippian, and the Kaskaskia sea covered most of the state. Its abundant life is now preserved in many fossiliferous limestone formations. This sea retreated in the late Mississippian.

During the Pennsylvanian and Permian Periods, the supercontinent Pangea assembled as Euramerica collided with Gondwana, a large continent composed of South America, Africa, Australia, Antarctica, and India. The collision produced the Appalachian Mountains, which resembled the Himalayas of today. Although far from the center of tectonic activity, New Mexico was affected by the collisional forces. Basins developed, and land was uplifted to become the Ancestral Rockies. The basins were filled with rising seas, this time part of the Absaroka transgression. Abundant life occupied not only the seas at this time, but also the land. Plants and animals, which first colonized land in the Silurian, had diversified to include forests of ferns and conifers inhabited by invertebrates, amphibians, and reptiles.

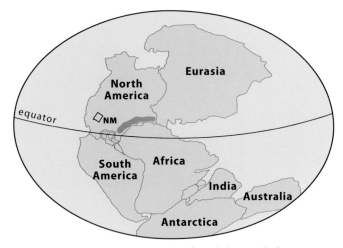

supercontinent Pangea

Appalachian Mountains

The continental collision that formed the Appalachian Mountains produced uplifts in New Mexico.

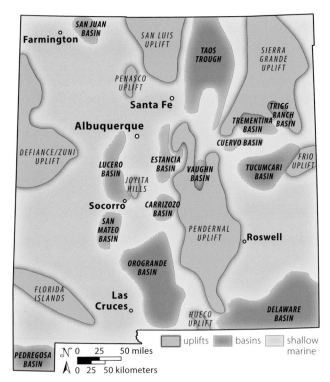

uplifts   basins   shallow marine

The Ancestral Rockies formed during the Pennsylvanian, creating local highlands and deeper-water basins. A warm, shallow sea submerged other parts of the state and limestone was deposited.

Limestones deposited in warm, shallow seas that once covered New Mexico in Pennsylvanian time are often exposed as sequences of gray rock layers, such as the Magdalena Group shown here. This photograph was taken about 1.5 miles west of High Rolls at the Tunnel Vista Observation Site along US 82 in the Sacramento Mountains.

Ripple marks created by flowing river water are often seen in stream deposits like the Abo Formation of Permian age, viewed here at Salinas Pueblo Missions National Monument. Hat for scale.

While marine sedimentation and the deposition of limestones dominated the Pennsylvanian Period in New Mexico, stream-deposited red beds and other terrestrial sediments became more abundant as sea level dropped and tectonic uplift continued during the Permian Period. By the end of the Permian, most of the state was above sea level. The exception was the southeast, where the Delaware Basin was surrounded by a major reef complex. During the Permian, New Mexico moved to a position about 10 degrees north of the equator, and the climate became significantly drier, causing the deposition of thick sequences of rock salt and gypsum in the southeastern part of the state as shallow seas evaporated.

New Mexico remained above sea level during the Triassic Period. Large rivers with wide floodplains flowed toward the northwest across the state. Earth's first dinosaurs appeared during the Triassic. Many skeletons of *Coelophysis* (pronounced see-low-fi-sis), a small carnivorous dinosaur that is the state fossil of New Mexico, have been excavated from rocks deposited by these major stream systems.

As Pangea broke apart to form the modern continents during the Jurassic Period, North America moved northward. New Mexico went from being located about 10 degrees north of the

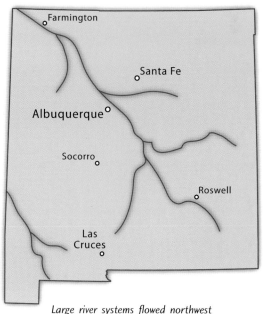

Large river systems flowed northwest across the state in the Triassic Period.

New Mexico was located at the edge of the Western Interior Seaway during the Cretaceous Period. As sea level fluctuated, varying amounts of the state were submerged under the sea.

equator to about 30 degrees north. Deserts are common at this latitude, and an erg, or sand sea, grew to cover the northern part of the state. The final rise in sea level to affect New Mexico, the Zuni transgression, created the Western Interior Seaway that bisected North America from the Gulf of Mexico to the Arctic Ocean. As sea level fluctuated during the Jurassic and Cretaceous, the coastline migrated across New Mexico. Many fossils are preserved in these Jurassic and Cretaceous coastal rocks, including dinosaurs, the plants that grew at the time, animals that shared the land with the giant reptiles, and the creatures that swam in the Western Interior Seaway.

The Laramide orogeny, a unique mountain building event that has long intrigued geologists, began in the latter part of the Cretaceous Period. Usually, mountains are built along the edges of tectonic plates; however, the Laramide orogeny formed the Rocky Mountains far inland from the active plate margin along the west coast of North America. While geologists still debate the details of this event, it was likely due to an oceanic plate subducting beneath the continent at a shallower than normal

Rocks deposited by rivers often include both fine-grained mudstone and shale that formed in the floodplain, as well as sandstone that was deposited in the main channel. Rivers in late Triassic time deposited the Chinle Group, viewed here at Ghost Ranch, where a reddish channel sandstone overlies the multicolored floodplain mudstones.

Sandstones deposited in large sand dunes by wind are characterized by large cross beds, like these shown in the Neogene-age Popotosa Formation in the Bosque del Apache National Wildlife Refuge.

angle. As the Rocky Mountains rose, the Western Interior Seaway receded, and seawater never again covered any part of New Mexico. The dinosaurs that had migrated along the seashore went extinct 66 million years ago when a large meteor struck the Earth.

The movement of tectonic plates continued uninterrupted into the Cenozoic Era, and the Laramide orogeny lasted until around 40 million years ago. The Colorado Plateau was also uplifted in the Cenozoic, although there is much debate about the exact timing of the event. Two pulses of major volcanism affected parts of New Mexico. The first, from 40 to 20 million years ago, was a sequence of explosive caldera-forming eruptions known as the Mid-Tertiary ignimbrite flare-up that created several volcanic fields, including the Mogollon-Datil and Bootheel. The second pulse of volcanism began about 10 million years ago and continues to the present. Several volcanic areas, including the Zuni-Bandera volcanic field, Valles caldera, and Raton-Clayton volcanic field, erupted during this time along the Jemez lineament.

The development of the Rio Grande Rift during the Cenozoic significantly shaped New Mexico's modern topography. A rift is an area where a continent is being pulled apart by tensional forces. Beginning around 36 million years ago, these east-west pull-apart forces began to affect the region, creating a conspicuous north-trending valley that bisects the state and extends north into Colorado and south into Mexico. Basalt erupted along the rift as the crust thinned, and sediment filled the growing basins. The rifting peaked between 16 and 10 million years ago and has since subsided without dividing the continent.

Because of this long and complex geologic history, New Mexico can be divided into six physiographic provinces: the Colorado Plateau, Southern Rocky Mountains, Rio Grande Rift, Mogollon-Datil volcanic field, Basin and Range, and High Plains. In this book, I combined the Mogollon-Datil volcanic field and Basin and Range because they both lie in the southwest portion of the state and overlap geologically. This book describes sixty sites that highlight the beauty and diversity of these different parts of New Mexico.

COLORADO PLATEAU

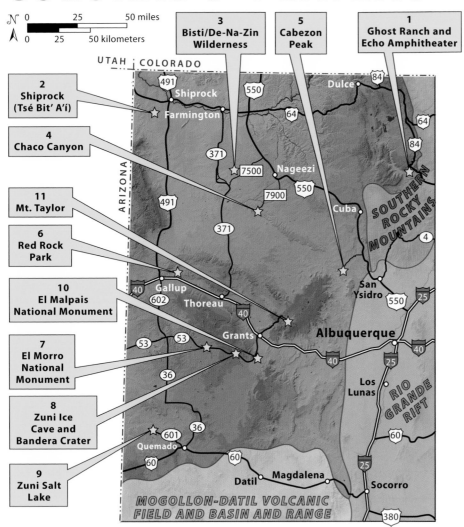

N
0   25   50 miles
0   25   50 kilometers

3 Bisti/De-Na-Zin Wilderness

5 Cabezon Peak

1 Ghost Ranch and Echo Amphitheater

2 Shiprock (Tsé Bit' A'í)

4 Chaco Canyon

11 Mt. Taylor

6 Red Rock Park

10 El Malpais National Monument

7 El Morro National Monument

8 Zuni Ice Cave and Bandera Crater

9 Zuni Salt Lake

UTAH | COLORADO
ARIZONA

Dulce
Shiprock
Farmington
7500
Nageezi
7900
Cuba
SOUTHERN ROCKY MOUNTAINS
Gallup
Thoreau
Grants
Albuquerque
San Ysidro
Los Lunas
RIO GRANDE RIFT
Quemado
Datil
Magdalena
Socorro
MOGOLLON-DATIL VOLCANIC FIELD AND BASIN AND RANGE

The vast open spaces and eroded multicolored rocks of the Colorado Plateau are some of the most iconic vistas of the American West, immortalized in many movies. The plateau, which extends well beyond northwestern New Mexico to include western Colorado, northern Arizona, and southern Utah, is a unique region with relatively undeformed, mostly flat-lying or very gently dipping sedimentary rocks. About 25 million years ago, these rocks began to be uplifted, eventually rising to an average elevation of around 6,200 feet above sea level. A consequence of this uplift was extensive erosion by rivers and streams, revealing the colorful layers of rock that would otherwise have remained buried and hidden from view. The exact mechanism that caused this uplift and its precise timing are still not fully understood, and numerous studies of this fascinating region are ongoing.

Ghost Ranch and Echo Amphitheater

NEW MEXICO IN THE DAYS OF THE DINOSAURS

Ghost Ranch is a private spiritual retreat surrounded by open space with hiking trails and other activities. Echo Amphitheater, a few miles north of Ghost Ranch, is part of Carson National Forest Recreation Area. The area's spectacular scenery inspired artists like Georgia O'Keeffe and has served as the backdrop for many movies. The colorful layers of rock also tell the story of New Mexico during the time of the dinosaurs.

Reddish siltstone and mudstone with white-to-tan sandstone at the base of the cliffs around Ghost Ranch are in the Chinle Group. It was deposited 228 to 205 million years ago in Triassic time in floodplains, channels, and tributaries of a large river flowing from Texas northwest across New Mexico. Overlying the Chinle Group, a prominent cliff that fades from red to white to yellow is the Entrada Sandstone, which formed from large sand dunes in a desert that covered much of the Four Corners region in Jurassic time. The pale-gray Todilto Formation, composed of limestone and gypsum, rests on the Entrada Sandstone. These rocks were deposited in a salina, an isolated body of saline water. As this salty water receded, a dry coastal plain formed with deposits of dark-red siltstone and sandstone of the Summerville Formation. On top of the Summerville is the tan Bluff Sandstone, another layer of rock representing a time when sand dunes covered the region. Dating to about 150 to 148 million years ago, in late Jurassic time, the pale-green to pink siltstone and sandstone of the Morrison Formation were deposited on a river floodplain.

During the Cretaceous, the area of Ghost Ranch was located at the edge of the Western Interior Seaway. A river that flowed toward this sea over a broad coastal plain deposited pale-red and green sandstone and conglomerate of the Burro Canyon Formation. Overlying this is the brownish Dakota Sandstone. The sandstone and shale of this formation were deposited along the shoreline of the seaway. As sea level rose, fine-grained sediments of the Mancos Shale accumulated on the seafloor, over the top of the shore deposits.

Ghost Ranch is located on US 84, 13 miles north of Abiquiu. Echo Amphitheater is 4 miles north of the Ghost Ranch turnoff.

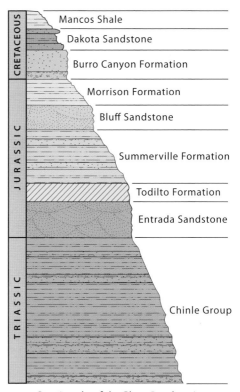

Stratigraphy of the Ghost Ranch region.

Colorful layers of rocks showing the Mesozoic stratigraphy of the Ghost Ranch area. The base is the Chinle Group, the prominent white cliff at the center is the Todilto Formation, and the brown rocks at the top are the Dakota Sandstone.

Numerous fossils have been discovered in the Ghost Ranch area, especially in the Chinle Group. The best known is *Coelophysis*, a 10-foot-long carnivorous dinosaur and the state fossil of New Mexico. It evolved in early Triassic time, one of the earliest dinosaurs. Other fossils include complete skeletons of the early carnivorous dinosaur *Tawa hallae*, crocodile-like phytosaurs, and *Vancleavea*, a semiaquatic armored reptile. Many of these fossils can be viewed at the Ruth Hall Museum of Paleontology, located at the Ghost Ranch Education and Retreat Center.

Echo Amphitheater offers a nice opportunity to walk through the reddish Entrada Sandstone, getting a close look at large cross beds that formed as wind shifted the sand and the dunes migrated across the ancient desert. At the end of the short trail is a natural amphitheater, eroded in part by a waterfall. In New Mexico's arid climate, this waterfall is usually dry. The amphitheater has also been shaped and enlarged by a process called spring sapping. Groundwater seeps out of the Entrada Sandstone directly above the underlying Chinle Group because the water cannot penetrate the impermeable mudstone. This water slowly dissolves the cements holding together the tiny sand grains that make up the Entrada Sandstone, gradually enlarging the amphitheater.

Echo Amphitheater has developed in the Entrada Sandstone.

Shiprock stands at the right, and one of its three radial dikes extends to the left. The eroded rock along the edge of the dike is Mancos Shale.

Shiprock (Tsé Bit' A' í)
THE DEEP PLUMBING SYSTEM OF AN ANCIENT VOLCANO

Towering about 1,600 feet above the surrounding desert, Shiprock is a prominent landform within the Navajo volcanic field, part of the Colorado Plateau that was volcanically active about 30 to 18 million years ago. Many textbooks use Shiprock as a classic example of a volcanic neck, which is where the magma of an ancient volcano flowed upward toward the surface. The remains of the volcano's plumbing system are revealed when the extinct volcano is eroded. While this is true of Shiprock, more details about the story make this iconic New Mexico landmark geologically fascinating.

Shiprock is composed of volcanic breccia, a collection of rock fragments created in explosive eruptions, and minette, a relatively rare igneous rock similar to basalt but containing abundant biotite and alkali feldspar minerals. About 27 million years ago, this minette lava rose toward the surface and encountered groundwater in the rock. The 1,200-degree Celsius minette flash-boiled the water, resulting in an explosion of steam and volcanic material that created a cone-shaped conduit filled with volcanic breccia and an explosion crater on the surface called a maar. Shiprock is part of the breccia-filled conduit, called a diatreme. Long, narrow bodies of igneous rocks, called dikes, squeezed their way through cracks in the rock surrounding the rising magma and today can be seen radiating from Shiprock. The former surface of the maar crater was about 3,300 feet above Shiprock. Erosion of the relatively soft Mancos Shale has revealed the breccia and dikes.

The best place to view Shiprock and one of the radial dikes is from Indian Service Road 13. Shiprock is a sacred site to the Navajo, so please stay on the main road and be respectful of the location.

explosive eruption cloud

fallout of ash and rock fragments

former land surface

eroded rocks

maar crater

eroded rocks

diatreme of volcanic breccia and minette

present-day erosional surface

Shiprock diatreme

minette lava rises, encounters groundwater in an explosive reaction

not to scale

Rising magma flash-boiled groundwater creating an explosive eruption and a maar crater. Erosion following the eruption revealed the cone-shaped diatreme beneath the maar and sculpted Shiprock into the shape seen today.

The minette (darker rock fragments) was brecciated in an explosive volcanic eruption. This rock is from another diatreme near Shiprock in the Navajo volcanic field. Pocket knife for scale.

13

A hoodoo of resistant sandstone stands above badlands eroded in soft shale.

Bisti/De-Na-Zin Wilderness
THE BEAST OF AN ANCIENT RIVER DELTA

If you venture into the arid, inhospitable Bisti Badlands of the Bisti/De-Na-Zin Wilderness today, you might have a difficult time imagining that around 70 million years ago, during the late Cretaceous, primitive birds flew in the canopy of lush forests along the banks of rivers while dinosaurs lumbered below. The rivers flowed eastward into the retreating Western Interior Seaway, a shallow ocean that once covered the central part of North America. Sediments deposited in the channels, floodplains, and deltas hardened to become predominantly sandstones and shales of the Fruitland Formation and Kirtland Shale.

A few of the organisms that died became buried in the sediments. If they remained buried for a long time, they were preserved as fossils. The Bisti Beast (*Bistahieversor sealeyi*), a relative of *Tyrannosaurus rex*, was discovered in the Bisti Badlands and excavated in the 1990s. The fossil is in the collection of the New Mexico Museum of Natural History and Science in Albuquerque, where a full-size robotic replica entertains visitors. Other dinosaurs excavated from the badlands include *Parasaurolophus*, *Pentaceratops*, and *Alamosaurus*, a sauropod that was one of the largest animals to inhabit North America. Fossils of crocodiles, turtles, lizards, fish, mammals, and plants are also present. In some areas, large logs that were carried by powerful, fast-moving rivers and eventually buried in sediment are preserved. In other places, petrified tree stumps are fossilized in their growth position.

Because the Bisti Badlands include soft, easily eroded shales and mudstones with some harder, more resistant sandstones in between, erosion has produced odd forms where resistant layers protect underlying soft layers. Known as hoodoos, these natural sculptures reflect the unique geologic history of the area.

To reach the Bisti/ De-Na-Zin Wilderness, follow NM 371 south from Farmington for 33 miles, then turn left on County Road 7290 and follow the signs to the parking area. Additional parking and good views of the badlands are available off County Road 7500.

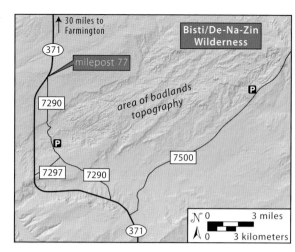

The multicolored rock layers in the badlands include black and gray mudstones and shales deposited in river floodplains, tan and brown layers of sandstones deposited in the river channels, and pebbly surfaces of yellow that are the eroded remnants of thin sandstone layers. The reddish pebbles are a clinker deposit found in parts of the badlands where burning coal seams baked the surrounding sedimentary rocks.

Chaco Canyon
ANCESTRAL PUEBLOAN CULTURE AMIDST FOSSILIFEROUS ROCK

About 85 to 75 million years ago during the Cretaceous Period, the area around Chaco Canyon was at the edge of the Western Interior Seaway. Sediment was deposited in lagoons, swamps, barrier islands, deltas, and estuaries of a broad coastal plain, resulting in a variety of sandstone, mudstone, shale, and coal. The two main rock units at Chaco Canyon are the Menefee Formation and Cliff House Sandstone, both part of the Mesaverde Group. The late Cretaceous coastal environment preserved in the Mesaverde Group was teeming with a variety of life. The Menefee Formation, which erodes into shaly badlands, is particularly fossiliferous, including petrified wood as well as the remains of turtles, dinosaurs, and crocodilians. Some of the petrified wood is so well preserved that you can see termite burrows. The Cliff House Sandstone includes fossil bivalves and ammonites, as well as rare vertebrate fossils of mosasaurs, plesiosaurs, and sharks.

Chaco Canyon was carved into these rocks by the Chaco River drainage over the past few million years. The 15-mile-long canyon is 2,100 feet wide and 500 feet deep, but it was once about 100 feet deeper. A thick layer of sediment fills the bottom of the canyon. Long-term climate cycles have resulted in numerous periods of sediment deposition and erosion. Chaco Wash, an intermittent stream today, joins the main drainage of the Chaco River at the west end of Chaco Canyon, which flows north into the San Juan River.

People likely settled around Chaco Canyon as early as 13,000 years ago, but the earliest well-dated human occupation was around 900 BC. Early inhabitants may have been attracted to the canyon by the rock shelters that form at the base of the cliffs at the contact between the easily eroded Menefee Formation and the cliff-forming Cliff House Sandstone. Differential weathering of these same formations also attracted Ancestral Puebloans to build their cliff dwellings in the alcoves of Mesa Verde National Park in Colorado.

At Chaco Canyon, isolated pithouses, or semisubterranean dwellings, appeared around AD 200, and about 300 years later villages of pithouses were built. Around AD 700, pueblo building began, and Chaco emerged as a major center of Ancestral Puebloan Culture around AD 850. The largest pueblos were built starting around AD 1050 using local sandstone. The timber was hauled here from the Zuni and Chuska Mountains over 45 miles away. Between AD 1130 and 1150, Chaco Canyon's prominence faded. Archaeologists debate the reasons, which likely include a major drought in the region as well as cultural changes.

To visit Chaco Canyon, turn onto County Road 7900 from US 550, 3 miles east of Nageezi or 50 miles west of Cuba, and follow the signs to the Chaco Culture National Historical Park. It is 21 miles to the park from the turnoff, including 13 miles of very rough dirt road.

Pueblo Bonito, the largest of the Ancestral Puebloan ruins at Chaco Canyon, lies at the base of a cliff of the Cliff House Sandstone. In 1941, a large piece of this cliff, known ominously as Threatening Rock, collapsed and destroyed thirty rooms of the pueblo. Debris from this event can be seen at the base of the cliff at right.

A petrified stump (left) in the Menefee Formation and a bivalve (right) in the Cliff House Sandstone. —National Park Service photos

Cabezon Peak
A VOLCANIC NECK

Rising more than 1,100 feet above the Rio Puerco valley is the imposing edifice of Cabezon Peak, the most prominent volcanic neck of the Mt. Taylor volcanic field. Volcanic necks are erosional remnants that provide a view of the interior of an ancient volcano. Basaltic lava erupted from a vent in the volcanic field about 2.6 million years ago. The initial eruptions were mildly explosive due to gases contained in the lava, forming a cinder cone of small pieces of basalt full of holes from gas bubbles. Late-stage eruptions were gas poor, so lava no longer exploded from the vent. It pooled in the center of the cone and solidified. Much more resistant to erosion than the bubble-filled basalt pieces, this solidified lava remains even though the rest of the volcano was worn away.

The lava at Cabezon Peak is an excellent place to view columnar jointing. These vertical fractures form when lava starts to cool at spots known as cooling centers. Forces pull inward toward the centers because cooling material contracts, or shrinks, perpendicular to the nearest cool surface. When the cooling centers are evenly spaced, polygonal columnar joints are formed. Typically, the more uniform the substance that is cooling, the more evenly those centers form. The large hexagonal columns at Cabezon Peak formed in pooled lava, perpendicular to the pool's base.

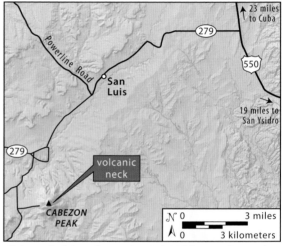

Cabezon Peak is easily seen from US 550 between San Ysidro and Cuba. To get closer, follow NM 279 west toward San Luis.

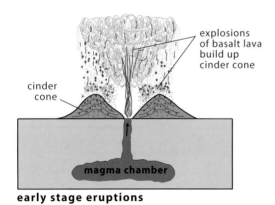

explosions of basalt lava build up cinder cone

cinder cone

magma chamber

early stage eruptions

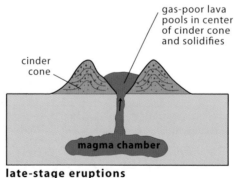

gas-poor lava pools in center of cinder cone and solidifies

cinder cone

magma chamber

late-stage eruptions

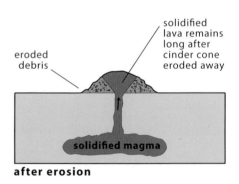

solidified lava remains long after cinder cone eroded away

eroded debris

solidified magma

after erosion

Initial mildly explosive eruptions built a cinder cone that later filled with a pool of lava that solidified.

Columnar joints, like these at Cabezon Peak, form as lava cools and contracts.
—Photograph by Kelsey McNamara

The Cabezon Peak volcanic neck is a prominent landmark of the Mt. Taylor volcanic field.

Navajo Church (Church Rock) is a colorful landmark sculpted from rocks of the Morrison Formation.

6 Red Rock Park
A Desert Trapped in Stone

The towering cliffs and multicolored rocks at Red Rock Park, east of Gallup, were a popular filming location for Hollywood Westerns in the 1940s and 1950s. The perfect backdrop for telling stories about cowboys and outlaws also reveals a chapter of New Mexico's epic geologic history. The rocks include six major sedimentary units of the Colorado Plateau, deposited from Triassic to Jurassic time.

As you drive toward the park from the south, you cross the brick-red Chinle Group, which was deposited in floodplains, channels, and tributaries of a large river flowing from Texas to Nevada in the Triassic Period. Unfortunately, this formation is covered by recent sediment and soil and is only poorly exposed

in a few places. After the Chinle Group was deposited, there was a period of erosion that lasted about 40 million years at this location.

Around 165 million years ago, in the Jurassic Period, sediments started to accumulate above the eroded surface, becoming the Entrada Sandstone, the prominent red-orange cliffs in Red Rock Park. The surface between these two units is known as an unconformity, a gap in the rock record that indicates a period of erosion. Looking closely at the Entrada Sandstone, you can see large cross beds that formed when windblown grains of sand accumulated as layers in ancient sand dunes. The top of the Entrada Sandstone grades into the pale-gray limestone of the

Todilto Formation. This limestone formed when the Entrada desert was flooded by a salina, a body of oxygen-poor, very salty water. Overlying the Todilto Formation are interbedded pink, white, and red-brown sandstone, siltstone, and shale of the Summerville Formation that formed in the shallow water along a coastal plain. Desert conditions returned to the region with the deposition of the Bluff Sandstone, another sandstone with large cross beds characteristic of dunes.

The youngest rock unit in Red Rock Park is the Morrison Formation, still of Jurassic age. The older (and stratigraphically lower) part of this unit, the Recapture Member, includes red siltstone and yellow-to-white sandstone beds. Parts of this member were deposited by a river, while others contain the cross beds of sand dunes. The dune deposits are absent from the younger (and stratigraphically higher) part of the Morrison Formation, showing that the climate became wetter. A large river flowed to the northeast, and its network of tributaries deposited a complex sequence of sediments.

Hiking trails in Red Rock Park wind through all these multicolored rocks and provide excellent views of the surrounding landscape. Just outside the park to the north is a prominent landmark known as Navajo Church, also called Church Rock. The lower part of this sculpted rock is cross bedded sandstone of the Recapture Member capped with Morrison Formation river sandstone. Navajo Church can be viewed from the parking lot near the park post office, but the Church Rock hiking trail provides the most spectacular views.

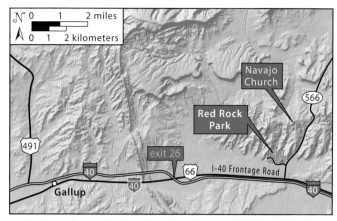

Red Rock Park is located about 7 miles east of Gallup. There is no direct exit from I-40 to NM 566, so you must take the I-40 frontage road (US 66) to get there. From the east, take exit 33 to the frontage road; from the west take exit 26.

Entrada Sandstone shows cross beds formed in sand dunes.

El Morro National Monument

Rising about 200 feet above the surrounding desert, El Morro is well named because *morro* means "nose" or "promontory" in Spanish. This landform, also known as Inscription Rock, boasts more than two thousand petroglyphs, names, dates, and messages carved into the soft sandstone. The oldest documented signature belongs to Don Juan de Oñate, who dated his message "16 April 1605," although some of the Native American petroglyphs pre-date this. Atop the mesa are the Atsinna Ruins, a large pueblo that was home to between 1,000 and 1,500 people. It was built in the late 1200s and occupied for only about 75 years. A reliable pool of water—rain and snowmelt sheltered from evaporation by shade at the base of the cliffs—made El Morro a popular stop for travelers through the desert.

El Morro is composed of Zuni Sandstone with a cap of Dakota Sandstone. The Zuni Sandstone formed about 160 million years ago in Jurassic time as part of a dune field that covered a large portion of the southwestern United States. The Zuni is a stratigraphic equivalent to the Entrada Sandstone and Bluff Sandstone in other parts of the Colorado Plateau. Sea level rose into Cretaceous time, and by about 96 to 95 million years ago, the shoreline of the Western Interior Seaway was located nearby. Rivers flowing to this sea deposited sandy sediment that became the Dakota Sandstone.

The top of the Zuni Sandstone was exposed to weathering for about 60 million years before the Dakota Sandstone was deposited on it. The weathering bleached the top of the Zuni Sandstone bright white. In addition, pieces of the weathered Zuni Sandstone can be found incorporated in the overlying stream deposits of the Dakota Sandstone.

A trail leads past the pool of water that drew travelers to El Morro and past many of the petroglyphs those travelers left behind. The trail climbs to the top of the promontory, where spectacular views overlook the surrounding landscape. The flat areas around El Morro are lava flows that erupted from the Zuni-Bandera volcanic field around 700,000 years ago. The silhouettes on the horizon to the east are cinder cones of the volcanic field. As the trail atop El Morro winds past the Atsinna Ruins, you might also notice some tinajas, also called desert potholes, eroded into the bedrock. These natural depressions capture water and, while not large, have historically been important sources of water in the desert.

Small white pieces of the weathered Zuni Sandstone were picked up by flowing streams and incorporated into the overlying Dakota Sandstone. Pocket knife for scale.

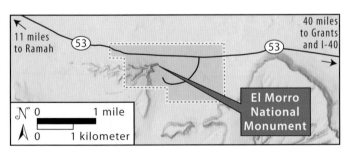

El Morro, in El Morro National Monument, is located 43 miles west of Grants on NM 53.

An inscription left by Captain Richard H. Orton, who fought in New Mexico and Texas during the Civil War. He later became Adjutant General of California.

El Morro rises prominently above the surrounding desert. The Dakota Sandstone at the top overlies the bright-white layer of the Zuni Sandstone.

A short hiking trail leads to an overlook into the Bandera Crater.

Zuni Ice Cave and Bandera Crater
YEAR-ROUND ICE IN THE DESERT

On a hot summer day in the high desert, the last thing you'd expect to find is ice. Zuni Ice Cave, a fascinating natural ice-box with year-round ice, owes its existence to recent volcanic activity. About 10,000 years ago, a vent eruption built a 430-foot-high cinder cone with a large crater, Bandera Crater. The eruption also produced a large basalt lava flow that covers 40 square miles. Within the lava flow is an 18-mile-long lava tube that formed when the outside of the lava flow cooled and solidified, but the inside continued moving and eventually flowed completely away, leaving a cavern behind. Much of the lava tube at Bandera Crater has collapsed.

Due to the unique orientation of the collapsed lava tube, freezing temperatures remain inside year-round. In the winter months, sun shining on the entrance of the cave heats it, and the warmer air rises, creating air circulation that pulls frigid air from inside the cavern. The cold air freezes water dripping from above into a mass of ice. During summer, the sun is at a higher angle so its rays never reach the cave, and cold air stagnates inside, preserving the ice. The temperature does not reach above 31 degrees Fahrenheit in the cave.

A half-mile trail leads to an overlook, where the cinder cone and its 650-foot-deep crater can be viewed. Along the trail, you can see tree molds that formed as lava cooled around tree trunks. The extreme heat burned away the wood, leaving behind openings in the lava flow in the shapes of the trees. Both pahoehoe and aa lava are present around the crater, as well as other volcanic features, such as a spatter cone where lava splashed out of a small vent. The Zuni Ice Cave is found at the end of a 400-yard-long trail. Numerous steps lead down to the ice.

Zuni Ice Cave and Bandera Crater are accessed via NM 53 about 25 miles south and west of exit 81 on I-40. The site is privately owned and has an admission fee.

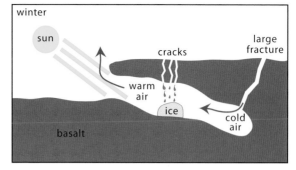

Air circulation patterns at the Zuni Ice Cave vary with the season, maintaining freezing temperatures year-round.

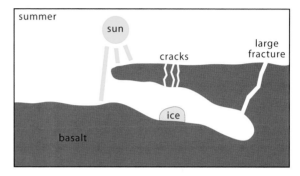

Ice accumulating in the collapsed lava tube.

Zuni Salt Lake

SACRED HOME OF THE SALT MOTHER

In 1598, when Don Juan de Oñate was exploring New Mexico, he discovered a location he described as "one of the most noted and best salt pans that Christians have discovered." He was referring to Zuni Salt Lake, which fills the base of a maar volcano in the Red Hill–Quemado volcanic field. Maar volcanoes form when rising magma encounters shallow groundwater that it flash-boils into steam. The resulting explosion creates a crater in the Earth's surface surrounded by volcanic debris. Zuni Salt Lake is 1 mile in diameter and surrounded with 150-foot-high crater walls.

Volcanic activity at this location began about 13,400 years ago with explosive magma-water interactions that created the maar and produced ash that was deposited as far as 5 miles away. As the eruption progressed, a circle of solidified magma called a ring dike prevented further water-magma interaction. The magma rose to the surface and can be seen as small lava flows and spatter. The final phase of the eruption formed three cinder cones that rise from the crater floor.

Water in the lake comes from surface runoff and saline springs that rise along faults. The groundwater obtains salt from the Yeso or Supai Formations in the subsurface. During the late Pleistocene, New Mexico experienced a wetter climate that allowed brackish water in the lake to support diatoms, algae, ostracods, and snails. As the climate warmed and the region became more arid following the end of the Pleistocene, around 11,700 years ago, the lake shrank to a third of its earlier size and

A view of Zuni Salt Lake and its three cinder cones from the west side of the crater.

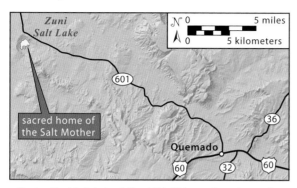

To view Zuni Salt Lake, follow NM 601 west from Quemado. This is a sacred site to the Zuni, so please stay on the road and be respectful of the location.

became much saltier. Today, Zuni Salt Lake has an average depth of about 3 feet. Total dissolved solids equal 206,000 parts per million (ppm), much saltier than seawater, which is 30,000 to 40,000 ppm. A small saline pool that has about 100,000 ppm total dissolved solids occupies the crater of the largest cinder cone. In these very salty waters, only certain types of bacteria and algae, brine shrimp, and shore flies survive.

Zuni Salt Lake is important to many Native American tribes, especially the Zuni, who consider the lake the sacred home of the Salt Mother (or Salt Woman) and have gathered salt from its shores for more than one thousand years. In 1877, the US Government established the Zuni Reservation and did not include the lake. Thus, from about 1910 to the 1970s, commercial extraction of salt using solar evaporation was conducted at the lake. In 1978, however, the US government ordered the lake to be returned to the Zuni, and in 1985 the land was deeded to the Zuni Pueblo.

Gray volcanic ash deposits blanket the area around Zuni Salt Lake.

El Malpais National Monument

YOUNG, HAWAIIAN-TYPE VOLCANISM

In Spanish, *el malpais* means "the bad country." Early explorers gave an area of west-central New Mexico this name due to the jagged, forbidding black surfaces of the numerous lava flows that cover about 950 square miles of land. While bad country for explorers, it is one of the best places to view young, Hawaiian-style volcanism in the contiguous United States.

El Malpais is part of the Zuni-Bandera volcanic field, which is located where the Colorado Plateau transitions to the Rio Grande Rift. The Jemez lineament, a linear zone of weakness in deep basement rocks, intersects both. Basaltic volcanism has occurred in the area for more than 1 million years, but many of the volcanic landforms seen are younger than 60,000 years old. The most recent activity was the eruption of the McCarty's

Flow, which formed about 3,900 years ago and is New Mexico's youngest lava flow. Volcanic activity of the Malpais has been very slowly migrating to the northeast, which can easily be seen by looking at the amount of vegetation on the numerous lava flows. In the southwestern part of the Malpais, vegetation is well established. In the northeast, the basalt is almost barren of vegetation because there has not been enough time for it to grow on the young lava flows. While there is no evidence that volcanic activity will resume, it is still possible in the area.

The more than one hundred vents in the volcanic field have created many features characteristic of basaltic volcanism. Cinder cones form around a vent as magma rises and is ejected onto Earth's surface. Eruptions from cinder cones are usually visually stunning, either occurring as numerous small explosions of bubbly lava or as spectacular fire fountains jetting glowing lava hundreds of feet skyward. Basaltic volcanism also produces both pahoehoe and aa lava flows. Pahoehoe, characterized by a ropy or wrinkled surface, forms as the surface of very fluid lava begins to solidify but the rest of the lava continues to move, causing the top to wrinkle. Aa flows are characterized by a jagged, blocky surface that forms as slow-moving lava cools and contracts, and sharp pieces of rubble break off. One of the most interesting features of the Zuni-Bandera volcanic field are lava tubes, or caves. These form as the outside of a lava flow cools and solidifies, but lava within the insulated interior continues to flow. The liquid lava can flow entirely away, leaving long tunnels behind.

The lava flowed through and erupted within a landscape eroded in the classic layered sedimentary rock of the Colorado Plateau. La Ventana, located to the east of the national monument, is a large natural arch formed in the Jurassic-aged Zuni Sandstone. This arch is shaped in part by a weathering process known as frost wedging. Liquid water seeps into cracks within the rock and expands slightly when frozen during cold desert nights, slowly prying off pieces of rock and sculpting the arch. Spectacular vistas of Mt. Taylor (site 11), El Malpais, and miles of surrounding countryside can be viewed from the Sandstone Bluffs Overlook, which is atop Cretaceous-aged Dakota Sandstone.

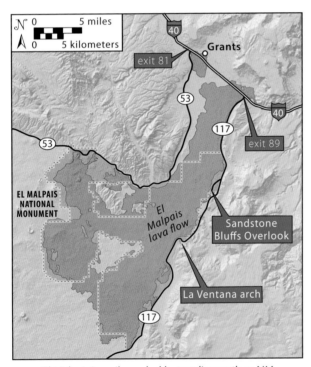

El Malpais is easily reached by traveling south on NM 117 from I-40 just east of Grants.

Site continues to page 30. ⟶

Looking northwest over the lava flows of El Malpais from the Sandstone Bluffs Overlook along NM 117.

Aa flows are characterized by a blocky, rubbly surface very different from the ropy pahoehoe (see site 32 for an example of pahoehoe). Vegetation is colonizing this aa flow, which erupted around 10,000 years ago.

La Ventana arch, viewed from NM 117, formed in the Zuni Sandstone, which was deposited as sand dunes during Jurassic time.

Mt. Taylor
11
A GIANT VOLCANO RISES HIGH

From about 4 million years ago to around 1.5 million years ago, a volcano developed in the area north of Grants. Mt. Taylor is a composite stratovolcano, meaning it was created by many different eruptions that produced a variety of volcanic rocks. Some eruptions produced thick and viscous rhyolite, andesite, or trachyte lava, while others spilled runny basalt. Some eruptions oozed viscous lava into domes while others were explosive, creating clouds of pyroclastic ash and pumice. Mt. Taylor is composed of layers of lava flows, pyroclastic rocks, and debris flows of broken volcanic material.

Despite significant erosion over the past 1.5 million years, Mt. Taylor still rises 11,301 feet above sea level. Estimates of the volcano's pre-erosion elevation vary, but it might have been as high as 14,000 feet above sea level. Today, the top of the volcano has a large, amphitheater-like crater that opens to the east. This crater may have formed by a lateral blast similar to the 1980 eruption of Mt. St. Helens, or it may have been created by erosion alone.

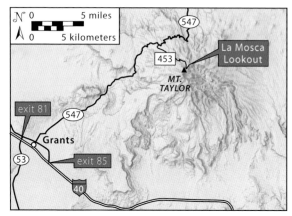

Mt. Taylor can easily be seen from I-40 around Grants. For a closer view, take NM 547 north from Grants. Turn right on Forest Service Road 453 to get to La Mosca Lookout tower on the rim of the summit crater. It provides spectacular views of Mt. Taylor's volcanic landscape.

View of Mt. Taylor from the Sandstone Bluffs Overlook in El Malpais National Monument (site 10).

SOUTHERN ROCKY MOUNTAINS

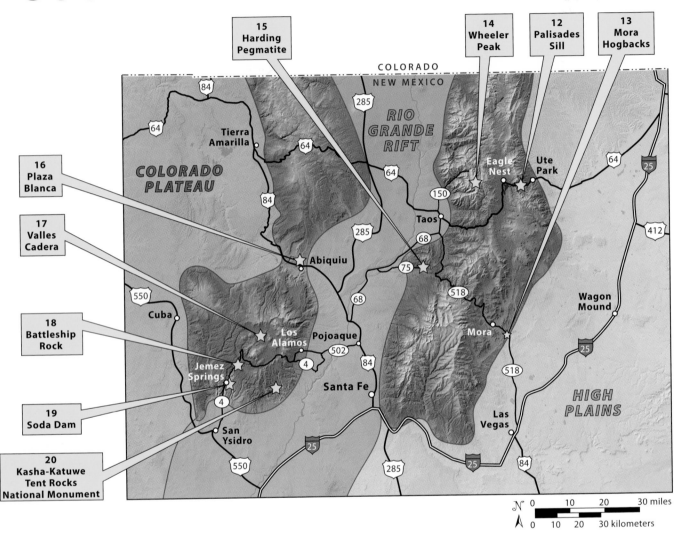

COLORADO
NEW MEXICO

15 Harding Pegmatite

14 Wheeler Peak

12 Palisades Sill

13 Mora Hogbacks

16 Plaza Blanca

17 Valles Cadera

18 Battleship Rock

19 Soda Dam

20 Kasha-Katuwe Tent Rocks National Monument

COLORADO PLATEAU

RIO GRANDE RIFT

HIGH PLAINS

Tierra Amarilla

Eagle Nest

Ute Park

Taos

Abiquiu

Cuba

Los Alamos

Pojoaque

Jemez Springs

Santa Fe

San Ysidro

Mora

Wagon Mound

Las Vegas

N

0   10   20   30 miles

0   10   20   30 kilometers

The Southern Rocky Mountains, where both the tallest peaks and oldest rocks in New Mexico are found, extend southward into New Mexico from Colorado as two mountainous areas separated by basins of the Rio Grande Rift. The Sangre de Cristo Mountains lie east of the rift valley, and the Tusas Mountains and Sierra Nacimiento lie to its west. This area was deformed and uplifted during the Laramide orogeny that occurred from about 70 to 40 million years ago. Rocks in the cores of the mountains record a suture zone, the Jemez lineament, where a large block of crust was added to North America about 1.7 to 1.6 billion years ago. Because of very limited exposures, most of what is known about this block comes from seismic reflection studies. The lengthy and complex history of these rocks since their addition to the continent is still being studied.

Palisades Sill
COLUMNAR JOINTS IN CIMARRON CANYON STATE PARK

US 64 between Eagle Nest and Ute Park follows the Cimarron River through Cimarron Canyon. The river cut its winding canyon through complex geology that includes Proterozoic metamorphic rocks, Paleozoic to Mesozoic sedimentary rocks, and younger igneous rocks that intruded all of the older rocks. One of the most spectacular places in the canyon is the Palisades Sill in Cimarron Canyon State Park. The rocks of these towering cliffs formed about 25 million years ago as magma squeezed its way between layers of older rock, creating a sheet-like horizontal intrusion known as a sill. The igneous rock of the sill contains visible crystals of plagioclase, quartz, and biotite within a fine-grained matrix, a rock known as a dacite porphyry. The crystals probably formed in the magma before it was injected, and the rest of the magma cooled too quickly for visible crystals to form, creating the matrix.

As this magma cooled and solidified, it contracted and fractured perpendicular to its cooling surfaces—the top and bottom of the sill. Its prominent vertical fractures are known as columnar joints. As water seeps into the joints and enlarges them through weathering, columns break and fall, creating piles of blocks at the base of the cliffs.

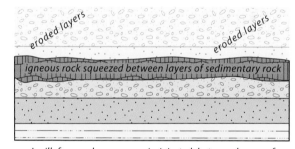

A sill forms when magma is injected between layers of sedimentary rocks. In the case of the Palisades Sill, the overlying rocks have eroded away.

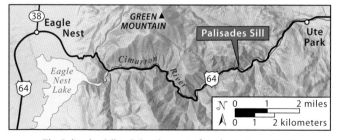

The Palisades Sill is 8.3 miles east of Eagle Nest on US 64.

The towering cliffs and columnar joints of the Palisades Sill are easily viewed from a roadside park.

Between Mora and La Cueva, NM 518 passes through a sequence of jagged ridges, called hogbacks, separated by narrow valleys. These rocks reveal a slice of New Mexico's geologic history and mark the eastern edge of deformation related to uplift of the Rocky Mountains. Beginning around 70 million years ago, at the start of the Laramide orogeny, the uplift of the Rocky Mountains began, and the flat-lying sedimentary rocks overlying the crystalline basement become steeply tilted. Millions of years of erosion removed the younger overlying rocks from the top of the modern mountains, revealing these basement rocks at the surface. In Mora, Quaternary sediments cover these old metamorphic rocks, but Proterozoic gneiss and quartzite are exposed in the surrounding hills and mountains.

Heading east from Mora along NM 518, you cross a fault zone and enter the sedimentary rocks that were tilted during the Laramide orogeny and dip toward the east. The rugged hogback ridges and valleys result from differential weathering of the varied rock types. Sandstone and limestone tend to be resistant to erosion and form the sharp hogback ridges. Mudstone and shale are easily eroded and form the valleys.

The hogbacks become progressively younger to the east. The oldest rock unit encountered is the Mississippian Arroyo Peñasco Group. Mostly limestone, these rocks were deposited when the region was submerged under a shallow sea. In some places, the rocks contain fossils of crinoids and brachiopods. Overlying these limestones is a sequence of Pennsylvanian units, including the Sandia, Porvenir, and Alamitos Formations. These include layers of shale, limestone, sandstone, and conglomerate. These different rock types formed in various depositional environments and reflect the complex tectonics of the Ancestral Rocky Mountains that involved both the uplift and erosion of highlands, as well as the subsidence of basins and sediment deposition within them. During the Permian Period, rivers flowing from the Ancestral Rocky Mountains deposited the Sangre de Cristo Formation. Nonmarine deposition continued into the Triassic Period as shale and sandstone of the Santa Rosa Sandstone and Chinle Group were deposited in river channels, floodplains, lakes, and deltas.

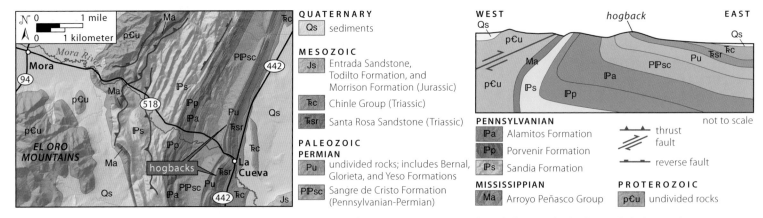

The Mora hogbacks are located on NM 518 between Mora and La Cueva. A cross section through the Mora hogbacks reveals faulting and folding that occurred during the Laramide orogeny and caused the originally horizontal sedimentary rocks to become steeply tilted.

Looking to the north at the Mora hogbacks. Mora and the oldest rocks are to the left while La Cueva and the youngest rocks are to the right.
—Photograph by Marli Miller

Permian Period sandstones and mudstones dip steeply to the east at the Mora hogbacks.

Wheeler Peak viewed from the north.

Wheeler Peak
New Mexico's Glaciated High Point

Rising to an elevation of 13,161 feet above sea level, Wheeler Peak is the highest point in New Mexico. It is named after George M. Wheeler, who led a survey of the region in the 1870s. Rocks of Wheeler Peak were originally intrusive igneous and volcanic rocks that were emplaced and erupted around 1.7 billion years ago in a volcanic arc. Later, these rocks were buried deep in the Earth and metamorphosed into gneiss and amphibolite. They were uplifted during the late Cretaceous to Eocene Laramide orogeny and now form the core of the mountain.

Wheeler Peak is part of the Sangre de Cristo Mountains, the southernmost range of the Rockies. During the Pleistocene ice ages, the snowline in the Sangre de Cristo Mountains was about 3,000 feet lower than today, which allowed glaciers to form on mountains at and above 12,000 feet in elevation. Some of these alpine glaciers grew to become more than 500 feet thick and carved amphitheater-like cirques and wide, U-shaped valleys into the rock. These glaciers also left behind thick deposits of sediment called moraines and created small lake basins known as tarns high in the mountain valleys. Some of the moraines are at elevations of around 10,500 feet, telling geologists that the ice

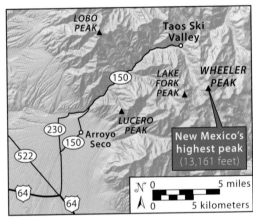

Location map of Wheeler Peak.

spread down from the peaks to at least this elevation. Although the climate is much warmer today than it was during the Pleistocene Epoch, glaciers have not completely disappeared from the mountain. Rock glaciers, slow-moving masses of rock fragments cemented together by ice, still exist.

Wheeler Peak is part of the Wheeler Peak Wilderness Area, so only hiking trails reach the summit. Two of the most popular, the Williams Lake Trail and the Bull of the Woods Trail, begin in the Taos Ski Valley in a forest of pine, spruce, and aspen. As the trails wind to higher elevations, the trees become stunted and fewer in number until alpine tundra begins above about 12,000 feet. At the peak, only some scrubby bushes, grasses, sedges, and lichen grow, allowing for spectacular views from the top of New Mexico. Marmots, a squirrel relative, scurry around rocks in summer and whistle warnings to their friends. Another wary, whistling animal that clambers around the heights of Wheeler Peak is the pika, a shy relative of the rabbit. It gathers grasses during the summer to sustain itself through the winter because, unlike the marmot, it does not hibernate.

Cirques and moraines viewed on a satellite image of Wheeler Peak.

A cirque on the southeast side of Wheeler Peak.
—Photograph by Patrick Alexander, Creative Commons 1.0

The Harding Pegmatite
ENORMOUS CRYSTALS OF UNIQUE MINERALS

As a magma body cools, hot fluids are the last part to decrease in temperature. The magma becomes enriched in volatiles (the gas forms of carbon dioxide and water), allowing very large crystals to grow. The magma can also become enriched in rare elements, providing the right chemistry for unique minerals to crystallize. Rocks composed entirely of large crystals are called pegmatites. The Harding Pegmatite, in the foothills of the Sangre de Cristo Mountains north of Santa Fe, formed about 1.3 billion years ago as volatile-rich magma squeezed its way into older metamorphic rocks of the Vadito Group.

As the magma cooled from the edges toward the center of the magma chamber, eight well-defined zones of minerals developed. The upper edge of the pegmatite contains the beryl zone, the massive quartz zone, and the quartz-lath spodumene zone, which sports 6-foot-long, white spodumene crystals. The core of the pegmatite includes the spotted rock zone, the rose muscovite-cleavelandite zone, and the cleavelandite zone. The lowest part of the pegmatite is the perthite zone and the aplite zone. The zones at the top and at the bottom are not identical because of the gravitational settling of crystals, and because the last material to cool is very chemically active, so it can corrode and replace minerals that formed earlier.

Rock was first mined from the Harding Pegmatite in the 1920s when a pale-purple mica called lepidolite was extracted for its high lithium content. Lithium was used in the ceramics industry and for making heat-resistant glass. From 1942 to 1947, Harding became the only mine in the world to produce major amounts of microlite, a tantalum-bearing mineral. Tantalum was needed during World War II for use in radios, vacuum tubes, synthetic rubber, and various metal alloys. The last period of mining occurred between 1950 and 1958, when four men and a mule named Beryl made Harding a leading producer of the mineral beryl, which is an ore of beryllium used in making metal alloys.

The very distinctive contact between the white pegmatite (bottom) and dark amphibolite, a metamorphosed basalt (top), is obvious above one of the entrances to the mine.

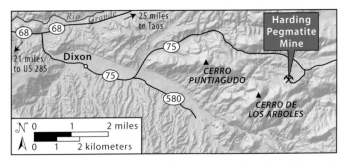

To get to the Harding Pegmatite, take NM 75 east from Dixon. The road to the mine is a right turn just past mile marker 8. This road is not well marked. Permission to visit the site must be obtained from the Department of Earth and Planetary Sciences at the University of New Mexico.

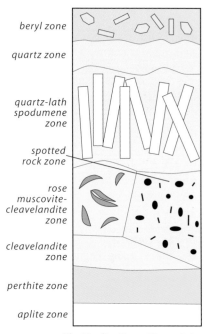

beryl zone

quartz zone

quartz-lath
spodumene
zone

spotted
rock zone

rose
muscovite-
cleavelandite
zone

cleavelandite
zone

perthite zone

aplite zone

The Harding Pegmatite contains eight basic zones containing different minerals that formed as the pegmatite magma cooled. Exact thicknesses of and relationships among these zones varies considerably across the pegmatite.

These large spodumene crystals are in the quartz-lath spodumene zone. Note the top of the rock hammer for scale.

For many years, the stark white and colorful pink and purple rocks of the Harding Pegmatite were owned by geology professor Dr. Arthur Montgomery, who leased them to the University of New Mexico for educating future geologists. When Dr. Montgomery decided he wanted to permanently donate the property to the university, a major problem arose. He held both patented and unpatented mining claims, which are governed by different laws, and the donation became a legal nightmare. Eventually, because the site contains so many interesting and unusual minerals, an act of Congress was signed into law by President Jimmy Carter in 1978 to ensure the fascinating site would be preserved, protected, and available for scientific study.

A mineral specimen from the Harding Pegmatite containing quartz (clear), spodumene (white), and a lithium mica (purple). The sample is about 3 inches long.

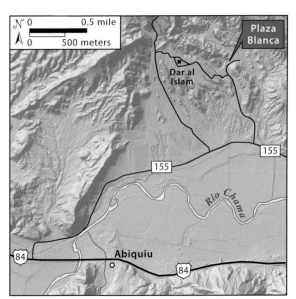

To get to Plaza Blanca from US 84, turn north on County Road 155 just west of Abiquiu. Turn left about 2.3 miles down the road at a large gate topped with the words "Dar al Islam." The gate will open as you approach slowly. At 0.6 mile down this road, a turnoff to the right leads to Plaza Blanca.

Plaza Blanca
AN ARTIST'S INSPIRATION

Georgia O'Keeffe, a twentieth-century artist, made her first trip to New Mexico in 1929 and moved there permanently in 1949. From a window of her Abiquiu home, she could look to the stark, white cliffs of Plaza Blanca. The clear blue desert skies and contrasting pale rocks inspired her to create paintings that captured the quiet beauty of the landscape she called "the White Place."

Rocks at Plaza Blanca are part of the Abiquiu Formation, layers of sediments composed mostly of volcanic particles. Their story begins about 25 million years ago, when a massive volcanic eruption created the Questa caldera north of Taos and deposited the Amalia Tuff. Around this time, rivers and debris flows laden with this fresh volcanic material flowed southward and deposited it at Plaza Blanca, creating a thick sequence of white and pale-gray tuffaceous sandstone with some conglomerate, as well as thin layers of pale-orange and pink mudstone. While the majority of this sediment is of volcanic origin, with abundant pieces of pumice and ash-flow tuff, the conglomerate layers also contain quartzite, schist, gneiss, and granite from the Proterozoic basement rocks to the north. Near Plaza Blanca, a lava flow close to the top of the Abiquiu Formation was radiometrically dated to around 19 million years ago, indicating that deposition of these volcanic-rich sediments had nearly ended by that time.

While most of the sediment at Plaza Blanca is derived from volcanic material, there are conglomerate layers that include cobbles of Proterozoic basement rocks weathered from the Sangre de Cristo Mountains.

Hiking trails lead around the sculpted rocks.

Sunlight on the stark white rocks of "the White Place" inspired artist Georgia O'Keeffe.

41

Herds of elk can often be seen grazing in Valle Grande, a large grassy valley within the ponderosa pine–forested Jemez Mountains. The flat valley is part of the Valles caldera, a giant 13-mile-wide crater formed in a violent volcanic eruption (see map on page 43). Calderas form when a large amount of magma erupts and the land above the magma chamber collapses into the empty space. Other examples of large, young calderas that formed during eruptions of supervolcanoes include Long Valley in California and Yellowstone in Wyoming.

The caldera-forming eruption occurred about 1.25 million years ago. A massive amount of rhyolite lava exploded from a giant magma chamber, forming the Bandelier Tuff, a deposit of ash and pumice that covered parts of New Mexico and sur-rounding states. Not long after the eruption, the movement of underground magma bulged the rocks upward, forming a resur-gent dome that is now Redondo Peak. Following the formation of Redondo Peak, thick, viscous rhyolite lava oozed onto the caldera floor and formed several volcanic domes. Obsidian, a glassy rock that cooled so quickly from the erupting magma that crystals did not have time to form, was prized by Native Americans for tool-making. Because the ice-age climate of New Mexico was cooler and wetter, lakes occupied the valley at least four times during the Pleistocene Epoch. Silt and mud settled to the lake bottom, filling in irregularities and becoming the very uniformly flat valley floor.

While the last eruption in the Valles caldera occurred about 40,000 years ago, magma is still underground, heating the rocks, which in turn heat the groundwater. The heated water rises and emerges as hot springs. Because magma is still present, geologists consider this volcano dormant, not extinct. It could erupt again; we just don't know when.

An outcrop of obsidian is located about 4.5 miles east of the junction between NM 4 and NM 126. Rock hammer for scale.

Valle Grande, the flat floor of the Valles caldera. The hill in the middle of the valley is Cerro la Jara, one of the volcanic domes that formed as viscous rhyolite lava oozed from a small volcanic vent after the caldera-forming eruption.

Battleship Rock

A PROMINENT LANDMARK OF WELDED TUFF

About 50,000 years ago, an explosive eruption from the Valles caldera produced a pyroclastic flow, a turbulent mixture of ash, pumice, and hot volcanic gases that raced down a canyon carved by the ancestral Jemez River. Because this volcanic material was still extremely hot when it was deposited in the canyon, the ash fused together forming a rock called welded tuff, or ignimbrite. Later, streams carved new channels through the softer sedimentary rocks on either side of the hard, welded tuff, leaving Battleship Rock standing 200 feet above its surroundings. The Jemez River and San Antonio Creek have since sculpted it into a triangular prow where they converge. The rock is an example of inverted topography, where the rock filling a former topographic low became a topographic high.

Spence Hot Springs, about 2 miles north of Battleship Rock, is another reminder of the area's volcanic past. The springs emerge from a contact between the Battleship Rock ignimbrite and the underlying Abo Formation. The water is 100 to 109 degrees Fahrenheit. Popular soaking pools terraced into the hillside can be reached by a half-mile hike.

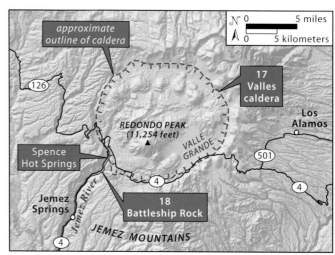

To visit Valles caldera, drive along NM 4 between Jemez Springs and White Rock. Battleship Rock is located along NM 4 just over 5 miles north of Jemez Springs.

Jutting out of the mountains like a ship cutting through the ocean waves, Battleship Rock is composed of hardened volcanic debris called welded tuff, or ignimbrite.

The travertine at Soda Dam grew across the Jemez River, which flows through an opening in the dam.

Soda Dam
TRAVERTINE DEPOSITS OF A HOT SPRING

Although the Valles caldera volcano is not currently active, magma is still present in the area and heats groundwater. Some of this hot groundwater rises along faults and surfaces at places like Soda Dam, where fifteen hot springs and seeps actively deposit travertine, a rock composed of calcium carbonate. The travertine here grew across the Jemez River and looks like a dam, but the river flows through a small tunnel.

The Soda Dam travertine began forming about 7,000 years ago. Older travertine deposits at higher elevations on both sides

of the river are up to 1 million years old, which indicates hot springs have existed at this location since shortly after the cataclysmic eruption of the Valles caldera 1.25 million years ago.

Water in the springs originates from a 400-to-600-degree-Fahrenheit hydrothermal system within the Valles caldera. The water moves along the Jemez fault zone, a break in the surface rocks that developed over the deep zone of crustal weakness known as the Jemez lineament. The water mixes with groundwater and is discharged from the springs around Soda Dam at temperatures varying between 86 and 118 degrees Fahrenheit. This hot water contains elevated levels of calcium, magnesium, bicarbonate, sodium, chlorine, lithium, boron, and bromine, as well as arsenic and radium. Water originally flowed along the top of Soda Dam; however, in the mid-1970s part of the west side of the dam was blasted away to smooth the road. This altered the water flow and limited new travertine deposition on the dam. The main spring is now located in the cut created by the highway department. A second important spring, known as Grotto Spring, is located in a small cave at the east end of the dam near the river. Additional small thermal seeps occur at the base of Soda Dam.

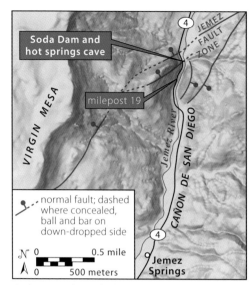

Soda Dam is located about 2 miles north of Jemez Springs on NM 4. Parking is available in turnouts along both sides of the road around the dam.

The main hot spring at Soda Dam is located on the west side of NM 4. Green algae coat the newly forming travertine.

20

Kasha-Katuwe Tent Rocks National Monument
HOODOOS IN VOLCANIC DEPOSITS

Kasha-katuwe means "white cliffs" in the local Puebloan language, an appropriate name for the steep, pale hoodoos northwest of Pueblo de Cochiti. These layers of rock capture a fascinating sequence of geologic events. About 7 to 6 million years ago, this part of New Mexico was the site of intense volcanic activity. Explosive eruptions of rhyolite from at least twenty small volcanoes formed the thick, layered sequence of rocks known as the Peralta Tuff. At least thirty-five eruptive events are recorded in the tuff. Volcanic material was eroded from rhyolite domes and deposited in layers to become the Cochiti Formation. Ancient soils formed within these sediment layers during calm, stable periods amidst all the violent eruptions. A fault with about 350 feet of offset shows this area experienced earthquakes as well.

At Kasha-Katuwe Tent Rocks National Monument, tent-shaped hoodoos form wherever a large, difficult-to-erode stone, called a capstone, shields softer rock beneath it from weathering and erosion. Eventually, the capstone falls, and the tent rock erodes away. Both water and wind have shaped these rocks, with water being the most important sculptor. When rain falls, some of the water finds its way into cracks, and over time it can widen them into deep, narrow slot canyons. Hikers can follow a popular trail at Kasha-Katuwe through a slot canyon where they can get a close-up view of the different layers—ash fall layers, pyroclastic deposits, and surge deposits—within the Peralta Tuff. Ash fall layers form when ash settles out of the atmosphere from an eruption cloud. These deposits are usually well sorted (all the particles are almost the same size) and blanket the landscape. Pyroclastic flow deposits form when a mixture of hot gases and volcanic material is explosively erupted from a volcano. These deposits are usually poorly sorted (they contain particles of all different sizes) and are deposited in valleys. Pyroclastic surges are similar to pyroclastic flows, except they contain more volcanic gases and less rock, so they are lower density and not constrained to valleys. Surge deposits are moderately sorted and commonly contain cross beds.

Scattered around the site are small black pieces of obsidian. Known as Apache tears, these obsidian pieces are eroded from glassy obsidian clasts in the sedimentary beds that are interlayered with the volcanic tuff in the cliffs. As groundwater moves through these sedimentary beds, it hydrates the obsidian, forming perlite. When this hydration process does not completely penetrate a clast, it leaves a core of obsidian—the Apache tear. Because perlite erodes easily, it is preferentially weathered, leaving the Apache tears behind. Because Kasha-Katuwe is a protected site, collecting Apache tears is not permitted.

The conical tent on the left still has the large rock that shields softer material underneath from weathering processes. The tent in the middle has two small capstones. The shielding rock on the right tent has fallen, leaving the softer material vulnerable.

This glassy black Apache tear is still encased in the surrounding material. While this specimen is from Arizona, it is typical of Apache tears found in the southwestern United States. —Photograph by Rob Lavinsky

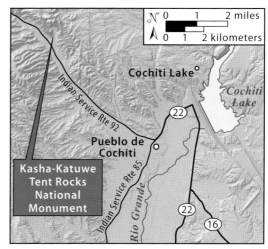

Kasha-Katuwe Tent Rocks National Monument is located just over 5 miles west of Pueblo de Cochiti on Indian Service Route 92.

The cliffs at Kasha-Katuwe Tent Rocks are composed of volcanic material deposited in explosive eruptions and sediment eroded from volcanic areas.

RIO GRANDE RIFT

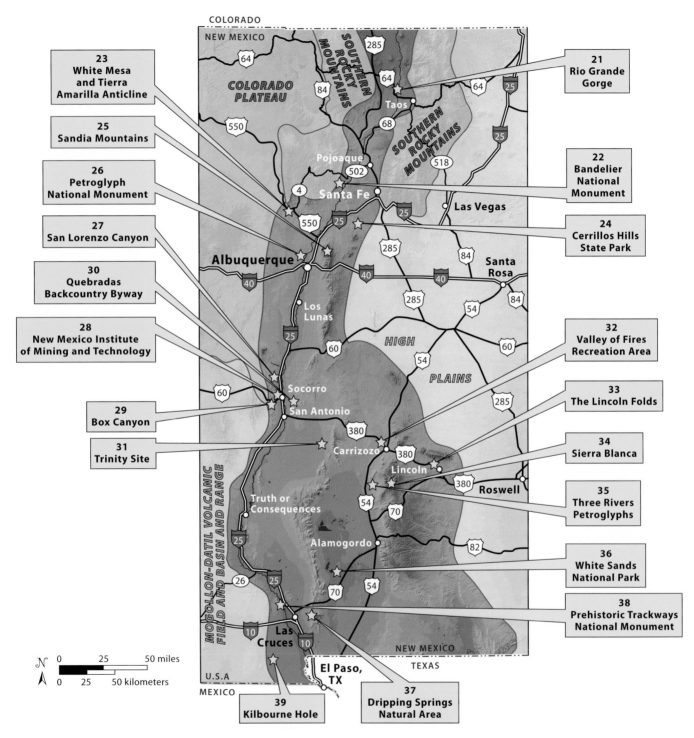

23
White Mesa and Tierra Amarilla Anticline

25
Sandia Mountains

26
Petroglyph National Monument

27
San Lorenzo Canyon

30
Quebradas Backcountry Byway

28
New Mexico Institute of Mining and Technology

29
Box Canyon

31
Trinity Site

21
Rio Grande Gorge

22
Bandelier National Monument

24
Cerrillos Hills State Park

32
Valley of Fires Recreation Area

33
The Lincoln Folds

34
Sierra Blanca

35
Three Rivers Petroglyphs

36
White Sands National Park

38
Prehistoric Trackways National Monument

37
Dripping Springs Natural Area

39
Kilbourne Hole

COLORADO
NEW MEXICO

COLORADO PLATEAU

SOUTHERN ROCKY MOUNTAINS

SOUTHERN ROCKY MOUNTAINS

Taos

Pojoaque

Santa Fe

Las Vegas

Albuquerque

Los Lunas

Santa Rosa

HIGH PLAINS

Socorro

San Antonio

Carrizozo

Lincoln

Roswell

Truth or Consequences

Alamogordo

MOGOLLON-DATIL VOLCANIC FIELD AND BASIN AND RANGE

Las Cruces

El Paso, TX

NEW MEXICO

TEXAS

U.S.A.

MEXICO

0   25   50 miles

0   25   50 kilometers

Extending from northern Mexico north into Colorado, the Rio Grande Rift is an area where North America began to split apart. This pull-apart action began about 36 million years ago in the south and progressed northward, with the onset of rifting near the New Mexico–Colorado border about 22 million years ago. The rifting produced numerous basins that collected thick sequences of sediment eroded from the surrounding mountains. Originally, these basins were isolated from one another, but about 600,000 years ago the Rio Grande connected them as it created a through-flowing stream from its headwaters in Colorado to its mouth in the Gulf of Mexico. Because the southern part of the rift has been spreading for a longer period of time, it is much wider than the northern part and merges with the Basin and Range as a series of valleys separated by mountains.

New Mexico's population is concentrated in the rift basins because aquifers in the basin-filling sedimentary layers provide water in an otherwise arid region. Santa Fe, Albuquerque, and Las Cruces all lie in rift basins. The rifting action is still occurring but has slowed significantly since the peak of activity between 16 and 10 million years ago. It appears North America will not split apart any time soon.

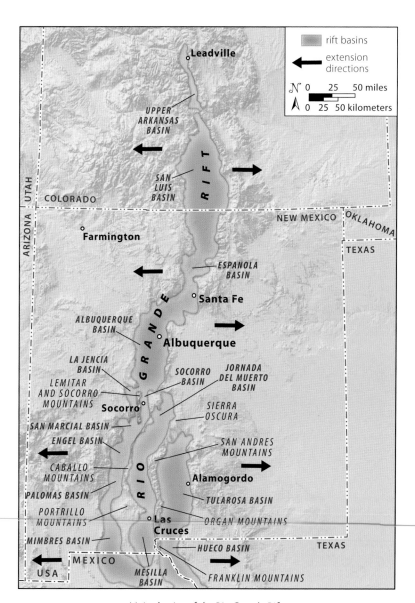

Major basins of the Rio Grande Rift.

49

21 Rio Grande Gorge
A Canyon through Basalt

About 75 miles long and up to 850 feet deep, the Rio Grande Gorge begins in southern Colorado and cuts southward toward Pilar, New Mexico. The river carved this steep, narrow canyon into a sequence of lava flows known as the Servilleta Basalt. These lava flows erupted between 4.8 and 2.8 million years ago from shield volcanoes and vents to the west near Tres Piedras. The fluid basalt lava spread across the landscape, flowing downhill and filling in low areas. The Rio Grande began cutting into the flat surface of basalt sometime between 800,000 and 440,000 years ago, when it captured the drainage of the San Luis Basin and its power increased. Regional uplift and higher precipitation during the Pleistocene also helped initiate down-cutting. Slumps, rockfalls, and other landslides have occurred as the river carves downward, creating numerous rapids within the gorge that challenge whitewater rafters.

Layers of the Servilleta Basalt visible to the north from the Rio Grande Gorge Bridge. —Photograph by Frank Karasti

One of the best places to view the lava flows and the canyon is on the Rio Grande Gorge Bridge, where US 64 crosses the river west of Taos. This long-span steel bridge was completed in 1965 and won an award for its beauty from the American Institute of Steel Construction the following year. The bridge includes sidewalks on both sides and small observation platforms for visitors to enjoy views of the bridge, the canyon it crosses, and desert bighorn sheep that live here.

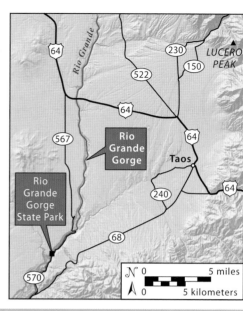

The Rio Grande Gorge west of Taos. US 64 crosses the gorge on the Rio Grande Gorge Bridge.

The Rio Grande Gorge Bridge with Wheeler Peak in the background.
—Photograph by Larry Maltby

51

On October 23, 1880, Cochiti Puebloans led archaeologist and ethnologist Adolph Bandelier to Frijoles Canyon to see their ancestral home. He described the canyon and ruins it contained as "The grandest thing I ever saw. A magnificent growth of pines, encina [oaks], alamos [cottonwoods], and towering cliffs, of pumice or volcanic tuff, exceedingly friable. The cliffs are vertical on the north side and . . . used as dwellings both from the inside, and by inserting roof poles for stories outside. Aside from the caves, there are ruins of a larger pueblo, immense estufas, round towers of two stories, etc."

The landscape that was so stunning to Bandelier is part of the Pajarito Plateau, which is the gently east-sloping flank of the Jemez Mountains that's cut by numerous deep canyons. A complex series of volcanic events shaped the landscape. About 3 million years ago, the Cerro del Rio Basalt erupted. Some of the magma interacted with groundwater and caused an explosive eruption of steam and volcanic material to create a maar volcano. Further eruptions built a cinder cone and produced basalt flows. By 2 million years ago, eruptions had ceased, and a period of major erosion ensued, developing a new drainage on the volcanic landscape. The Cerro del Rio Basalt and associated maar deposits can be viewed along the Falls Trail in Bandelier National Monument.

Around 1.85 million years ago, volcanic activity in the area resumed with the eruption of the Bandelier Tuff, which consists of three distinct members. The oldest is the La Cueva Member, a small leakage of magma from a large magma chamber. This unit is not well exposed in the national monument. A larger eruption about 1.6 million years ago spewed out the Otowi Member from the Toledo caldera. The eruption began with ash and pumice falling from the sky like rocky snow and covering the landscape under a blanket of volcanic debris known as ash fall. The volcanic activity concluded with the collapse of the eruption column, creating pyroclastic flows that filled the area's valleys with thick ash-flow (ignimbrite) deposits. This tuff-filled paleotopography can be seen down the canyon from the national monument visitor center, as well as at other places in the Jemez Mountains.

After about 400,000 years of quiescence, a third eruption formed the Tshirege Member, the youngest member of the Bandelier Tuff. This eruption, which created the Valles caldera 1.25 million years ago, also began with ash fall and concluded with ash-flow tuffs created by violent pyroclastic flows. This member

forms the flat surface known as the Pajarito Plateau. Following this cataclysmic event, streams carved deep canyons into the Tshirege Member, including Frijoles Canyon, where most of the Ancestral Puebloan dwellings Adolph Bandelier was so impressed with are located. As the stream in Frijoles Canyon cut downward, it eventually exposed the underlying Cerro del Rio Basalt downcanyon. The basalt forms the lip of Upper Frijoles Falls.

At some point following the most recent eruption, the Pajarito fault zone developed—the westernmost expression of the tensional forces of the Rio Grande Rift. About 650 feet of movement has occurred along this fault in the national monument, dropping the Pajarito Plateau down relative to the mountains to the west.

Text continues to page 54. ———>

Water drops over the resistant Cerro del Rio Basalt at Upper Frijoles Falls. To the left of the falls, layered reddish-brown rocks of the maar volcano eruption are exposed.

To get to the Bandelier National Monument Visitor Center, drive 8.5 miles south from White Rock on NM 4. Turn left onto Entrance Road and follow it for 3 miles.

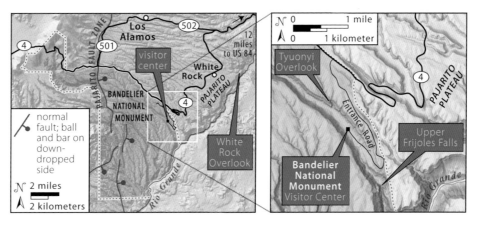

The Tshirege Member of Bandelier Tuff. Note the natural holes in the outcrop and the cavates carved by Ancestral Puebloans.

Visitors can observe a cavate by climbing this modern ladder.

While hunter-gatherers wandered the area for thousands of years, the earliest permanent settlements in Bandelier National Monument date to around AD 1150, when Ancestral Puebloans built homes out of blocks of tuff. They also carved rooms, called *cavates*, into the Tshirege Member of the Bandelier Tuff. Numerous natural holes occur in this member due to differential weathering of soft pumice clasts. Using digging sticks and stone tools, the Ancestral Puebloans enlarged holes into cavates, which usually were back rooms behind masonry structures. The Pajarito Plateau has the highest concentration of cavates in North America. In addition to these carved chambers, steps and trails were sculpted into the soft tuff.

The Ancestral Puebloans of Frijoles Canyon were an agricultural society who grew beans, corn, and squash and supplemented this food supply with hunting. They developed many techniques to maximize water retention for their crops and built check dams to hold rainwater and slow runoff. Pumice, because of its highly porous structure, was used as a water-holding mulch. The Ancestral Puebloans lived in the area until around 1550, when drought influenced their migration into the Rio Grande valley.

The remains of Tyuonyi, the main pueblo at Bandelier National Monument, constructed of blocks of tuff.

Looking west at White Mesa from US 550. The pale rocks at the top are the gypsum-rich Todilto Formation.

23 White Mesa and Tierra Amarilla Anticline

GYPSUM AND FOSSILS IN A PLUNGING FOLD

Just south of San Ysidro, US 550 winds past a towering, multicolored stone edifice known as White Mesa. The prominent white rock capping the mesa is the gypsum-rich Todilto Formation, which formed in the Jurassic Period when an isolated body of saline water evaporated. The red rocks at the base of the cliff are the Triassic-aged Chinle Group. Above them is the orange-yellow Jurassic-aged Entrada Sandstone. The stratigraphy of this area is very similar to that of Ghost Ranch (site 1), located about 60 miles north-northeast. Gypsum mining operations on

the mesa uncovered numerous ice-age fossils of horses, bison, camels, and deer dated to about 12,900 years of age. These animals fell into and were preserved in surface fissures created by pull-apart forces related to the Rio Grande Rift.

An excellent place to see the Todilto Formation, Chinle Group, and other rocks up close is at the White Ridge Bike Trails, where hikers are also welcome. These trails provide an excellent view of the Tierra Amarilla anticline, an upward arch also known as the San Ysidro anticline. Compressional forces of the Laramide

Looking north down the axis of the Tierra Amarilla anticline. The white rocks forming the top of the cliffs are the Todilto Formation. The mounds in the center of the eroded anticline are travertine deposits created by springs.

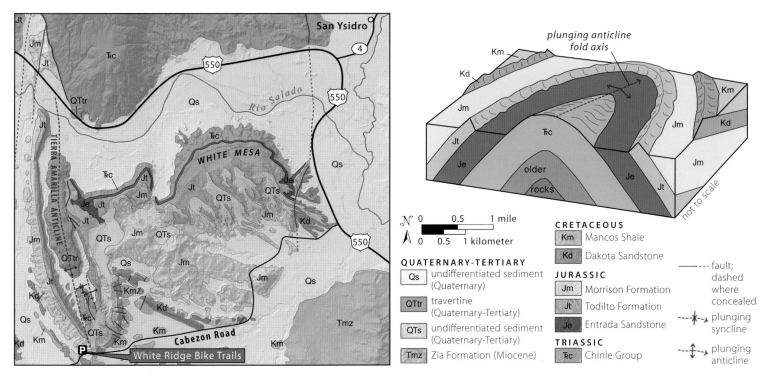

Geologic map and cross section of the Tierra Amarilla anticline. The map shows the curving outcrop pattern typical of plunging folds. Rock layers in a plunging anticline were bent by tectonic forces, and the hinge of the fold is tilted from the horizontal. Follow Cabezon Road 4.5 miles west from US 550 to reach the White Ridge Bike Trails.

orogeny bent and folded the rocks. The fold plunges south, so erosion has revealed a curving pattern in the multicolored layers. From the center to the edge of this anticline, the rocks are the deep-red Chinle Group, the white Todilto Formation, the red and brown Summerville Formation, the multicolored Morrison Formation, the tan Dakota Sandstone, and the dark-gray Mancos Shale. Beginning in the ice ages, springs welling up in the eroded center of the anticline formed mounds of pale travertine.

Astute readers will note that White Mesa features the Entrada Sandstone but the anticline does not. The Entrada Sandstone pinches out between the anticline and White Mesa, meaning it becomes thinner and disappears. It may have been here and then eroded away, or it may never have been deposited here.

In the Jurassic Period this region was at the southern edge of the sand dune field that created the sandstone. Between the Chinle Group and the overlying Todilto Formation is a gap in the geologic record known as an unconformity, a period when rocks were either eroded or not deposited.

Numerous fossils can be found in these Triassic to Cretaceous rocks. Plant fossils and the burrows of numerous organisms are common in the Dakota Sandstone. Giant dinosaurs like *Seismosaurus* and *Camarasaurus*—as well as gastroliths, stomach stones that helped some dinosaurs digest food—have been found in the Morrison Formation. In addition to the interesting ancient life, several modern species of plants endemic to New Mexico thrive in the gypsum-rich soil around White Mesa.

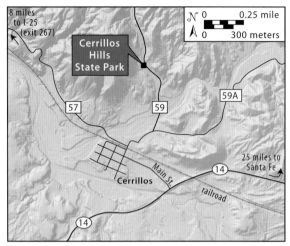

To get to the state park, take Main Street into Cerrillos from NM 14. Turn right at First Street, cross the railroad tracks, and at a Y, bear left onto County Road 59. The park is about a quarter mile down the road.

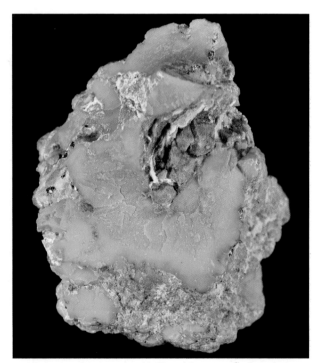

Native Americans extracted brilliant blue turquoise from the Cerrillos Hills long before Europeans came to New Mexico.

Cerrillos Hills State Park
MORE THAN 1,000 YEARS OF TURQUOISE MINING

Turquoise is important in many Native American cultures. It can represent creation, water, sky, bountiful harvests, strength, healing, and beauty. The blue-green stone was so important to Ancestral Puebloans at Chaco Canyon that they had a trade network for the stone that stretched across New Mexico, Colorado, Arizona, and Nevada. One of the most important sources of turquoise in New Mexico was Cerrillos.

The Cerrillos Hills are part of the Ortiz porphyry belt, an area of Oligocene igneous activity. Around 34 million years ago, shallow magma intruded between layers of Mesozoic to Eocene sedimentary rocks. About 4 million years later, dikes and stocks cut across the sedimentary rocks and earlier intrusions. Shortly thereafter, hydrothermal fluids flowing through cracks in the rocks created deposits rich in lead, zinc, copper, silver, and gold. Typical ore minerals include galena, sphalerite, chalcopyrite, and pyrite. Supergene enrichment, the alteration of these ore deposits by groundwater, led to the formation of the turquoise, which occurs in veins and as botryoidal coatings on rocks.

Mining for turquoise had begun at Cerrillos by at least AD 900, but possibly as early as AD 700. It became an important part of the Chaco Culture's trade network, and after that culture collapsed, people from the San Marcos Pueblo continued the mining operation. Around 1300, they began to extract galena to use for their distinctive lead-glazed pottery. The metal ores around Cerrillos were discovered by Europeans in 1581, when Fray Agustín Rodríguez and Captain Francisco "Chamuscado" Sánchez led an expedition to explore central New Mexico. The Spanish began mining silver at Cerrillos in the early 1600s but abandoned the area when indigenous Puebloans rose up against the Spaniards in the Pueblo Revolt of 1680. A lull in mining activity at Cerrillos through much of the 1700s and 1800s ended in 1879 when prospectors from Colorado rediscovered the metal wealth. Turquoise was also once again mined from 1890 to 1922 by the American Turquoise Company to supply Tiffany and Company with gem-quality stones. While mining continued into the twentieth century, especially during the world wars, the last major mining operation closed in 1975. Numerous hiking trails in Cerrillos Hills State Park wind through old prospects and mines, while even more mines are on private property in the surrounding hills.

The Cortez Mine is located along a 1-mile-long galena vein.

The hills around Cerrillos are dotted with numerous mines and prospect pits (circled).

Sandia Mountains
A Fault Block Exposes the Great Unconformity

As the sun sets and casts its glow on the pink granite of the Sandia Mountains on Albuquerque's eastern horizon, it is easy to see how the mountains might have earned their name. *Sandia* means "watermelon" in Spanish. The pink granite is the center of the watermelon, while the pale sedimentary rocks at the crest and the green forest growing atop are the rind.

The Sandia Mountains are relatively young. About 23 million years ago, pull-apart forces related to the Rio Grande Rift caused the Albuquerque Basin to sag downward along a normal fault while the Sandia Mountains fault block tilted eastward, eventually resulting in about 30,000 feet of displacement on the fault. The same rocks that are on the top of the Sandia Mountains are buried beneath thousands of feet of sediment in the basin.

The oldest rocks exposed in the Sandia Mountains are 1.65-billion-year-old metamorphic rocks (gneiss, schist, quartzite, and greenstone) that formed during the Mazatzal orogeny, when terranes were accreted to the growing continent. The majority of the mountains consist of the Sandia Granite, the magma of which intruded the metamorphic rocks and solidified deep underground about 1.42 billion years ago. After the granite was raised to the surface, it experienced a long period of erosion. A shallow sea encroached on New Mexico around 315 million years ago, in Pennsylvanian time, and deposited sediments on the eroded surface of the granite. The erosional surface between the sedimentary rocks and underlying granite is an unconformity. This particular unconformity, called the Great Unconformity, represents about 1.1 billion years of Earth history that's missing from the rock record. It separates Proterozoic-aged rocks of the continent's basement from younger sedimentary rocks and is seen throughout North America.

The Pennsylvanian sedimentary rocks at the crest of the mountains belong to the Sandia Formation and Madera Group. Numerous fossils of organisms that lived in the shallow sea can be found in the limestone units. Even younger sedimentary rocks, the colorful red and orange Abo and Yeso Formations, are found along the winding Sandia Crest National Scenic Byway that climbs 13 miles to Sandia Crest. The crest provides a great vantage point from which to see central New Mexico. Mt. Taylor (site 11), a young stratovolcano, can be seen due west. A clear day offers a long view down the Rio Grande Rift to the south. The tall mountains to the north are the Sangre de Cristos, the southernmost peaks of the Rocky Mountains.

Looking from Albuquerque eastward to the Sandia Mountains. The bulk of the mountains are Proterozoic granite capped with layers of Pennsylvanian sedimentary rocks. The location of the Great Unconformity is shown with a dashed line.

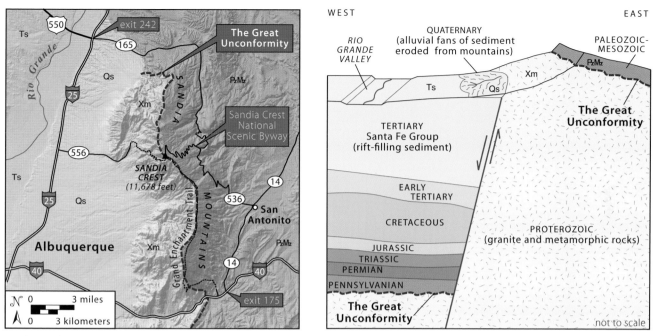

The Sandia Mountains are easily seen from anywhere in the Albuquerque region. To get to the crest, either take the Sandia Peak Tramway from Albuquerque or follow NM 536, the Sandia Crest National Scenic Byway, from San Antonito. The Great Unconformity is buried deep beneath the sediments and rocks in the Albuquerque Basin but revealed at the top of the Sandia Mountains.

Looking southward from Sandia Crest provides a great view of the Rio Grande Rift and the fault block mountains that line its eastern margin.

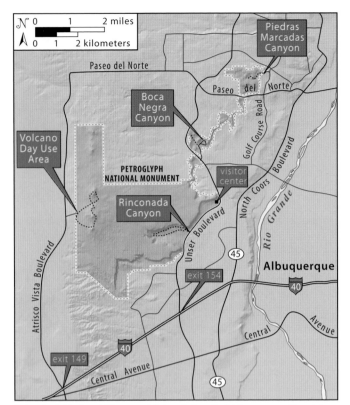

Petroglyph National Monument
ARTWORK ON A VOLCANIC CANVAS

26

Petroglyph National Monument is located west of Albuquerque. To get to the visitor center, take Unser Boulevard north from I-40 or south from Paseo del Norte. There are no petroglyphs at the visitor center; to view petroglyphs you must go to one of the trails at Rinconada Canyon, Boca Negra Canyon, or Piedras Marcadas Canyon. The Volcano Day Use Area can be reached from Atrisco Vista Boulevard.

West of Albuquerque, a prominent escarpment rises above the Rio Grande valley. This cliff is the eastern edge of the Llano de Albuquerque, a gently east-sloping surface that records not only the geologic history of the Albuquerque area, but also a chapter of human history. The story begins in the late Oligocene Epoch, when pull-apart forces began to create the Albuquerque Basin of the Rio Grande Rift. As major subsidence of the basin continued until around 5 million years ago, sediment continuously washed into it, accumulating a thickness of as much as 16,000 feet. This sequence of rift-filling sandstone, mudstone, and conglomerate is called the Santa Fe Group. The top of the Santa Fe Group is the Ceja Formation, deposited around 1.8 million years ago. The landscape then became stable, with little deposition and erosion, and a soil developed on its flat surface. Because of New Mexico's dry climate, the soil contained an accumulation of white calcite called caliche. The white, resistant caliche is quite prominent in places on the Llano de Albuquerque.

From 1.2 million years ago to 700,000 years ago, the Rio Grande developed into a major river flowing from Colorado to the Gulf of Mexico and linking the basins of the Rio Grande Rift. This change in drainage, as well as tectonic activity of the rift and climatic shifts, shaped the Rio Grande valley. The escarpment at the edge of the Llano de Albuquerque marks the western edge of the river's modern valley that it cut into the older surface.

These volcanoes, visible from the Volcano Day Use Area, erupted along a 5-mile-long, fault-controlled fissure.

Thousands of petroglyphs showing human, animal, and geometric figures were carved into weathered basalt blocks west of Albuquerque.

Between 210,000 and 155,000 years ago, basalt magma rose along a rift-related fault and erupted as fire fountains, volcanic spatter, and six basalt flows that cover part of the Llano de Albuquerque. The best place to view some of the volcanic vents is from hiking trails at the Volcano Day Use Area.

In the thousands of years since the volcanic activity, soft sediments underlying the basalt have been eroded, causing large blocks of the black lava to tumble down the Llano de Albuquerque escarpment. Most of the 25,000 petroglyphs found at Petroglyph National Monument are carved on these jumbled basalt rocks. This artwork was created by chipping away a dark coating of desert varnish (a mix of manganese oxide, iron oxide, and clay) to reveal the lighter rock beneath. The oldest petroglyphs date to around 2000 BC; however, most were created by Ancestral Puebloans between 1300 and 1680. A few of the youngest petroglyphs date to the Spanish colonial period.

27

San Lorenzo Canyon
A Slot through Debris Flow Conglomerate

Hidden in the mountains north of Socorro is a winding canyon with colorful rocks, eroded hoodoos, springs, and small waterfalls. On the drive into the canyon, a prominent ridge displays a classic angular unconformity—tilted rock layers capped by a horizontal layer. The tilted layers are the Popotosa Formation, conglomerates and sandstones that were deposited in streams and debris flows flowing from volcanic highlands to the west 18 to 7 million years ago. The sediments were flat lying when they were originally deposited in the Rio Grande Rift basin during the Miocene Epoch. As the Rio Grande Rift continued to split, these rocks were tilted and eroded before the horizontal layer of younger sediments was deposited on top. The surface between the two is the unconformity.

As you drive farther into the canyon, the road gets narrower, and the rock walls to either side become higher. Eventually, the 4WD road ends against a steep rock wall. The canyon continues beyond this barrier but must be explored on foot. Most of the rocks in the canyon belong to the Popotosa Formation. A few volcanic rocks, including basalt flows and the 28-million-year-old Vicks Peak Tuff, the hardened remains of a pyroclastic flow from the Nogal Canyon caldera to the west, can also be seen in the canyon. Several springs emerge where impermeable layers of rock force groundwater to the surface.

Running water carved San Lorenzo Canyon over the past million years, with the majority of the erosion occurring during the past 200,000 years. The canyon is prone to flash floods when rainstorms hit the nearby mountains.

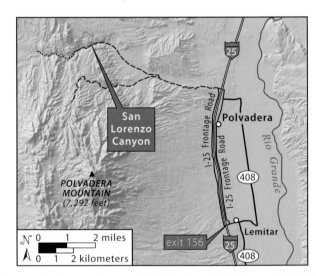

A small waterfall squeezes between rocks in the canyon after recent rain, continuing the erosion that shapes the canyon.

To get to San Lorenzo Canyon, take the Lemitar exit (156) from I-25. Follow the frontage road on the west side of the interstate north about 5 miles. At a T-junction, turn left onto the dirt road that leads to the canyon. The Bureau of Land Management has installed small brown signs providing directions along this road. I recommend you use a 4WD vehicle.

This prominent angular unconformity, where the tilted layers meet the flat caprock, is on the north side of the road that heads into San Lorenzo Canyon.

The road into San Lorenzo Canyon follows an arroyo prone to flash flooding. Tilted layers of the Popotosa Formation line the canyon walls.

Hoodoos have been carved into the Popotosa Formation over the past 200,000 years.

To get to the campus and museum, take either exit 150 or 147 from I-25 into Socorro. From the business route (California Street), turn west on Bullock Boulevard. The mineral museum is located at the corner of Bullock Boulevard and Leroy Place.

28 New Mexico Institute of Mining and Technology
MINERALS ON DISPLAY

In 1889, the Territorial Legislature established the New Mexico School of Mines to train engineers for the territory's growing mining industry. Socorro was chosen as the site for this new school due to its vicinity to several mining districts, including the famous Magdalena district (site 42) and the Socorro Peak district, which occupies the mountain just west of town, known locally as M Mountain. As more programs of study were added to the growing school, its name was changed in 1951 to the New Mexico Institute of Mining and Technology, which has grown into a world-renowned university for science and engineering.

The campus in Socorro is also home to the New Mexico Bureau of Geology and Mineral Resources, which maintains a world-class mineral museum. Established in 1889 as a collection of minerals used for teaching; the museum has since grown to include more than 18,000 specimens. While minerals from all over the world are on display, the museum includes special exhibits dedicated to minerals from mining districts, including copper minerals from Chino Mine (site 47) and gold specimens from the mountains west of Socorro.

The mineral museum at the New Mexico Bureau of Geology and Mineral Resources displays both local specimens from New Mexico as well as minerals from around the world.

This colorful specimen of wulfenite from the Bayard mining district near Silver City is one of thousands of minerals on display at the museum.

The Charles and Jessie Headen Center houses the New Mexico Bureau of Geology and Mineral Resources, including the mineral museum.

Looking west from Socorro to M Mountain, which rises to an elevation of 7,243 feet above sea level and exposes the northern edge of the 31.9-million-year-old Socorro caldera. Rocks that make up the mountain include Pennsylvanian sediments of the Sandia Formation and Madera Group; younger igneous rocks of the Luis Lopez Formation, including ash-flow tuffs, rhyolite dikes, flows, a sill, and a thick andesite lava flow; and debris flow deposits of the Popotosa Formation, all capped by the Socorro Peak Rhyolite.

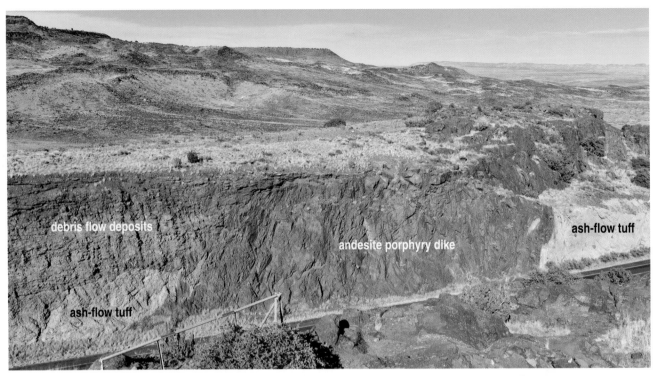

The dike, ash-flow tuff, and debris flow deposits exposed in this roadcut, where US 60 crosses Box Canyon, are part of the Luis Lopez Formation that was deposited in the moat of the Socorro caldera.

Box Canyon

A VIEW INSIDE A SUPERVOLCANO

West of Socorro, US 60 curves through white, purple, and reddish-brown rocks and passes Box Canyon, where the steep cliffs and jagged rocks provide challenging climbing opportunities. "The Box," as it is known locally, is within the 31.9-million-year-old Socorro caldera, which formed when about 250 cubic miles of volcanic material violently erupted from a supervolcano to create the Hells Mesa Tuff and left behind a 15-mile-wide caldera. The caldera is no longer visible on the surface, but geologists have pieced together information from different outcrops of volcanic rocks that were tilted and exposed by activity along the Rio Grande Rift.

Shortly after the caldera-forming eruption, underlying magma uplifted the central part of the caldera. There were a few small ash eruptions, and a rhyolite dome formed. The magma chamber feeding these eruptions then solidified. Conglomerate composed of andesite clasts and volcanic-rich sandstone began to accumulate in the caldera moat, the low area within a caldera and encircling the central uplift. In addition, volcanic activity resumed within the caldera with lava flows, the emplacement of some dikes, and the eruption of some ash-flow tuffs. All these moat-filling igneous and sedimentary units belong to the Luis Lopez Formation and are exposed in Box Canyon, along with a small volcanic vent that is partially obscured by recent rockfalls. Around 28.7 million years ago, another supervolcano eruption rocked the region. The Sawmill Canyon caldera destroyed the western side of the Socorro caldera when it erupted the La Jencia Tuff.

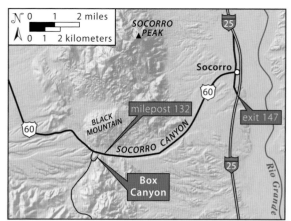

Box Canyon is located about 8 miles west of Socorro on US 60.

Most of the rocks at Box Canyon are andesite lava of the Luis Lopez Formation.

Quebradas Backcountry Byway
A DRIVE THROUGH GEOLOGIC TIME

The *Quebradas*, which means "breaks" in Spanish, is a rugged area of colorful rocks cut by numerous arroyos. You can explore the area along the 24-mile-long Quebradas Backcountry Byway, a gravel road that winds its way through the creosote, juniper, cholla, and ocotillo typical of the upper Chihuahuan Desert. Geology students from nearby New Mexico Tech (site 28) often visit the region to learn how to read the fascinating stories recorded in the multicolored layers of rock that have been twisted and deformed by tectonic activity.

Around 300 million years ago, during the Pennsylvanian Period, North America was located near the equator, and a warm, shallow sea covered the New Mexico region. The pale-gray limestone and shales of the Madera Group at the north end of the backcountry byway were deposited at this time; they preserve fossils of phylloid algae, brachiopods, crinoids, fusilinids, and other organisms. The dark-red Abo Formation, another prominent rock unit along the northern portion of the byway, was deposited by streams a little later, during the Permian Period. By this time the continent had slowly moved northward, and the streams flowed through a semiarid environment. Ripple marks and small cross beds created by the flowing water are preserved in some layers. Mud cracks in fine-grained layers indicate wetting and drying of clays on

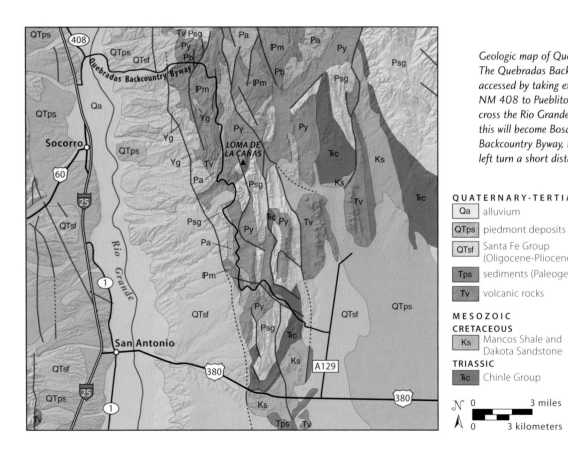

Geologic map of Quebradas Backcountry Byway. The Quebradas Backcountry Byway can be accessed by taking exit 152 from I-25. Follow NM 408 to Pueblitos Road and turn right and cross the Rio Grande. After a sharp right turn, this will become Bosquecito Road. The Quebradas Backcountry Byway, marked by signage, will be a left turn a short distance down the road.

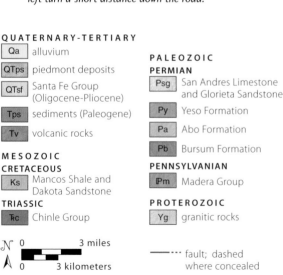

QUATERNARY-TERTIARY

Qa	alluvium
QTps	piedmont deposits
QTsf	Santa Fe Group (Oligocene-Pliocene)
Tps	sediments (Paleogene)
Tv	volcanic rocks

MESOZOIC
CRETACEOUS

| Ks | Mancos Shale and Dakota Sandstone |

TRIASSIC

| ᴦc | Chinle Group |

PALEOZOIC
PERMIAN

Psg	San Andres Limestone and Glorieta Sandstone
Py	Yeso Formation
Pa	Abo Formation
Pb	Bursum Formation

PENNSYLVANIAN

| ℙm | Madera Group |

PROTEROZOIC

| Yg | granitic rocks |

N   0 —————— 3 miles
     0 —————— 3 kilometers

- - - - fault; dashed where concealed

Looking east to Loma de la Cañas from the Quebradas Backcountry Byway. Rocks exposed include the Permian-age Yeso Formation, Glorieta Sandstone, and San Andres Limestone.

These rocks of the Yeso Formation show small thrust faults related to compressional tectonics of the Laramide orogeny as well as a normal fault related to tensional forces of the Rio Grande Rift. Located at 33°59'01"N, 106°45'42"W

streambanks and floodplains. The Abo contains abundant fossils of plants that grew along the streams, and trackways show that amphibians and reptiles prowled amidst the vegetation. As the continent continued to move northward, away from the humid equator, the climate continued to become drier. Times of extreme aridity are recorded by the Yeso Formation, which lies above the Abo. *Yeso* means "gypsum" in Spanish, and interbedded within the red, white, and tan layers are thick layers of gypsum, some preserving cubic impressions of salt crystals. Gypsum and salt precipitate when inland seas evaporate.

Toward the south end of the byway, rocks of the Triassic Chinle Group are exposed. These are mostly brown, dark-red, and purplish sandstones and siltstones deposited in river channels that migrated laterally across a muddy floodplain. A few

Cretaceous-aged rocks, located near the southern end of the byway, are tan Dakota Sandstone and darker layers of Mancos Shale. New Mexico was at the edge of the Western Interior Seaway, and sea levels were rising, so ocean bottom mud was deposited over the top of the sandy shore deposits. Many organisms, including clams and ammonites, lived in the sea and are now preserved as fossils.

In many places along the road, the rock layers have been folded and tilted from their original horizontal position. Some of this deformation occurred in the Pennsylvanian and Permian, when the Ancestral Rocky Mountains were formed, but much of it occurred during the more recent Laramide orogeny that created the modern Rockies. The tensional forces that formed the Rio Grande Rift also reactivated older Laramide faults.

Trinity Site

TESTING THE WORLD'S FIRST NUCLEAR WEAPON

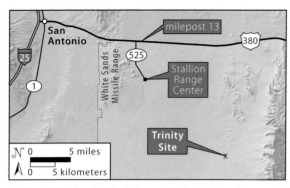

Just before 5:30 a.m. on July 16, 1945, a remote part of the Jornada del Muerto ("Journey of Death" or "Journey of the Dead Man") Desert near the base of the Sierra Oscura became the site where world history changed. Named Trinity by lead scientist J. Robert Oppenheimer, in reference to a John Donne poem he liked, this remote site was where the first atomic bomb, called Gadget, was detonated. With the enormous explosion, the world entered the Atomic Age.

Using a complex detonator, the 6 kilograms of plutonium in Gadget were set off on a steel tower 100 feet above the desert. The resulting blast, equivalent to 21 kilotons of TNT, created an 8-foot-deep depression about half a mile wide and almost completely demolished the steel tower. The brilliant light of the explosion was seen as far away as Santa Fe, New Mexico, and El Paso, Texas. Desert sand incorporated into the fireball was melted by its intense heat. These droplets of molten sand rained down and coated the surface of the area with a dark-green, glassy substance that was named trinitite.

Located on White Sands Missile Range, Trinity Site is only open to the public twice a year—the first Saturdays of April and October. To get there, follow US 380 east from San Antonio to the White Sands Missile Range Stallion Gate. Military personnel guide visitors to the site.

Heat from the atomic blast melted desert sand and created trinitite.

This stone monument was erected in 1965 to mark the location where the world's first nuclear weapon was detonated.

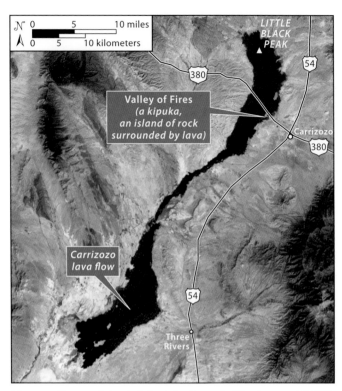

The recreation area is located about 4 miles west of Carrizozo on US 380.

Valley of Fires Recreation Area
A River of Lava

About 5,200 years ago, lava rose along a zone of weakness called the Capitan lineament and formed a new volcanic vent—Little Black Peak. A river of red glowing lava flowed southward from Little Black Peak and cooled, forming the Carrizozo Malpais. (*Malpais* means "bad country" in Spanish and is used for rough barren volcanic terrain in the Southwest.) This eruption was very similar to those on Hawaii, where lava slowly oozes from a volcano. Little Black Peak produced two lava flows during its short-lived eruption. The lower, older flow is 45 miles long, while the upper flow only extends about 16 miles. These flows were likely tube-fed, meaning lava was able to flow far from the vent, insulated inside a lava tube. Together, these flows cover approximately 127 square miles. It is estimated that it took twenty to thirty years of slow and steady lava eruption to form the malpais. In total, just over 1 cubic mile of lava was erupted. Numerous features typical of Hawaiian-type eruptions are present, including wrinkled pahoehoe

The lava in the foreground flowed from Little Black Peak, the small hill on the horizon.

Wrinkled pahoehoe lava is common at Valley of Fires. Hammer for scale.

lava, lava tubes (both intact and collapsed), tumuli (domed structures formed when slow-moving molten lava within a flow swells and pushes the overlying crust upward), and large fissures, all which formed while the lava was flowing.

For many years, it was thought these flows had formed as recently as 1,000 years ago. This idea was based on visual observations, such as iridescent surfaces that are typical of young pahoehoe, the lack of soil development on the lava flows, and the lack of vegetation growth. Cosmogenic isotope studies, which measure when rock surfaces are exposed to cosmic rays, show that the flows are much closer to 5,200 years old, still super young in geologic terms.

The Valley of Fires Recreation Area visitor center and campground are located on a *kipuka*, a Hawaiian term for an island of rock surrounded by lava. This rock is the Cretaceous-aged Dakota Sandstone, which was deposited as beach sand about 100 million years ago along the shoreline of the Western Interior Seaway.

Near vertical rock layers are part of the complex folding just north of Lincoln.

The Lincoln Folds
A GEOLOGIC MYSTERY

Lincoln, New Mexico, is probably best known as the location of the Lincoln County War, a violent conflict between rival merchants and cattlemen in the late 1870s. The small community is now home to the Lincoln State Monument, which preserves many of the buildings from that time, including the county courthouse from which Billy the Kid escaped in 1881. Lincoln is also the location of one of the Wild West's great geologic mysteries—the Lincoln Folds.

At the base of the cliff just north of the town, easily visible from US 380, the sedimentary rocks of the Yeso Formation are conspicuously folded. Above this complexly folded formation of Permian age are undeformed layers of the Glorieta Sandstone and San Andres Limestone, which also date to the Permian. Exactly how these folds formed is unknown. Numerous hypotheses attempt to explain the origin of these folds, including soft-sediment deformation during deposition of the Yeso Formation, landslides causing rotation in blocks of rock, forces related to igneous intrusions in the area, and deformation during the Laramide orogeny. You might think that the compression related to the Laramide orogeny would fold the overlying rocks as well, but different types of rocks react differently to stress. The Yeso is composed of hard limestone layers interbedded with soft mudstone, siltstone, and gypsum that could have facilitated the folding. Research into the origin of the folds is ongoing.

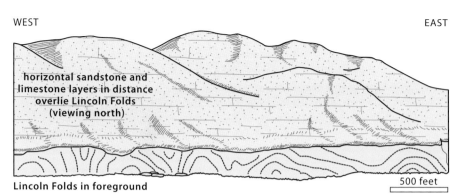

WEST   EAST

horizontal sandstone and
limestone layers in distance
overlie Lincoln Folds
(viewing north)

Lincoln Folds in foreground   500 feet

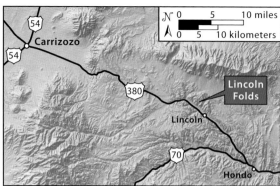

Lincoln is located on US 380, 33 miles east of Carrizozo.

Beds within the Yeso Formation are tilted and folded in various directions, while layers of the overlying Glorieta Sandstone and San Andres Limestone in the cliff above are horizontal.

Horizontal rocks overlie the complexly folded rocks of the Yeso Formation at Lincoln.

Sierra Blanca
AN OLDER VOLCANO CORED BY A YOUNGER VOLCANO

34

Sierra Blanca, a prominent peak visible throughout the Tularosa rift basin, was already a mountain before it was uplifted even more along a normal fault on the east side of the rift basin. The mountains surrounding the peak are composed of rocks of the Sierra Blanca Igneous Complex, assembled about 37 to 34 million years ago during numerous eruptions from a group of stratovolcanoes. This igneous activity also created hundreds of dikes—long, narrow bodies of magma that squeezed their way into cracks of older rocks as they were pushed away from the main magma chamber. These dikes are visible in roadcuts around Sierra Blanca.

The 11,981-foot peak of Sierra Blanca is composed of the Three Rivers stock, a younger body of intrusive igneous rock ranging in composition from syenite to granite. This magma intruded the older volcanic rocks about 28 million years ago. Its age and geochemistry are similar to a tuff deposit in the Tularosa Basin, suggesting the magma erupted at the surface as well, and the Three Rivers stock is the eroded remains of a magma chamber that erupted explosively to create a caldera.

Erosion has shaped the igneous rocks of Sierra Blanca since the mountain's fiery origin. Steady erosion and weathering by rainwater removed as much as 2 miles of rock from the surface, revealing these rocks that originally formed deep underground. More recently, during the Pleistocene ice ages, small glaciers carved valleys and deposited moraines of jumbled sediment.

Called ´Dzil gais ´ání by the Mescalero Apache, Sierra Blanca is one of four mountains sacred to the tribe. (The others are the Guadalupe Mountains, Three Sisters Mountain, and Oscura Mountain Peak). According to legend, in the midst of a violent thunderstorm at Sierra Blanca, White Painted Woman gave birth to two sons, Child of Water and Killer of Enemies. When these children grew to manhood, they killed monsters that were threatening the Earth and saved all human beings.

Looking east toward Sierra Blanca from Three Rivers Petroglyphs (site 35).

No roads lead to the summit of Sierra Blanca; however, following County Road 532 to Ski Apache gets very close. Because this is a sacred site, access to the mountain peak requires a permit from the Mescalero Apache tribe.

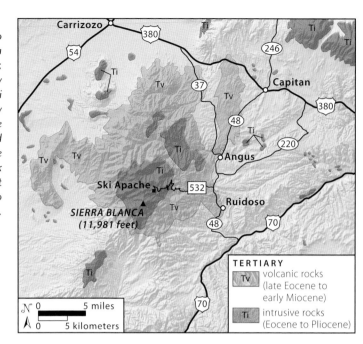

The lighter-colored dike, located on County Road 532 about 0.1 mile east of the junction with Forest Road 127A, squeezed into the darker rock as magma and then cooled.

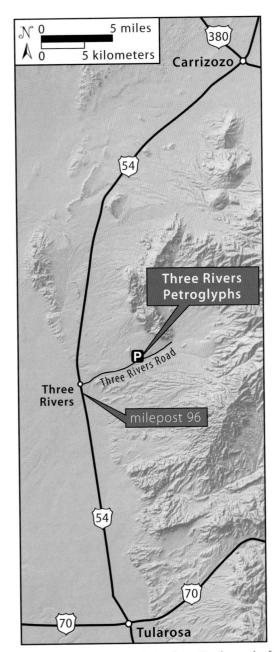

Three Rivers Petroglyphs
ANCIENT ART CAPTURED IN STONE

The Mogollon people, a farming culture, occupied parts of Mexico, New Mexico, Texas, and Arizona from around AD 200 to AD 1400. In addition to growing corn, beans, and squash, the Mogollon people supplemented their diet by hunting deer, rabbits, and birds with a new technological invention—the bow and arrow. Another advancement of the Mogollon people was clay pottery, which they decorated with different designs. Within the large Mogollon cultural group, there were numerous branches, including the Jornada Mogollon who lived in the Tularosa Basin. On the east side of the Tularosa Basin, on a ridge with a fine view of Sierra Blanca (site 34), are more than 21,000 petroglyphs carved by the Jornada Mogollon people between AD 900 and AD 1400. They used stone tools to chip away dark desert varnish from the gray rocks to create images of humans, birds, fish, other animals, plants, and many abstract designs and geometric patterns.

The gray igneous rock, a type known as trachybasalt, contains large crystals of black hornblende. About 36 million years ago, when it was still liquid magma, it squeezed its way between older layers of rock, eventually cooling and solidifying into a sill, the geologic name of an intrusion parallel to rock layers. This igneous activity was part of the complicated sequence of events that formed the Sierra Blanca Igneous Complex. Once exposed at the surface, a dark layer of desert varnish slowly built up on the rocks. This varnish is a thin coating of manganese, iron oxides, and clay. Exactly how it forms is debated, but it likely involves windblown dust, aerosols, and microbial activity.

To reach Three Rivers Petroglyphs, drive 17 miles north of Tularosa (or 28 miles south of Carrizozo) on US 54. Turn east on Three Rivers Road and drive for about 5 miles.

Petroglyphs at the Three Rivers site include figures of humans, animals, and geometric patterns.

81

Covering around 250 square miles, White Sands is the largest gypsum sand dune field in the world. The story of how this vast area of sand dunes formed begins long ago, even before dinosaurs roamed the Earth. In the Permian Period, over 250 million years ago, this part of New Mexico was located at the edge of a sea. The arid climate caused massive amounts of seawater to evaporate and form thick layers of gypsum. Starting about 36 million years ago, as tensional stress pulled the area apart to form the Rio Grande Rift, the Tularosa Basin subsided as the surrounding mountains were uplifted. During the last ice age, when the climate of the area was cooler and wetter, a large lake known as Lake Otero filled the Tularosa Basin. The ancient gypsum deposits, exposed in the uplifted mountains, were dissolved by rain and groundwater and carried to the lake. As the ice age drew to a close and the climate became warmer and more arid, Lake Otero dried and gypsum once again crystallized from the evaporating water. Today, a small remnant of Lake Otero exists as ephemeral Lake Lucero, which fills with water after heavy rains. New gypsum continues to precipitate when this water evaporates.

The earliest gypsum dunes began forming about 24,000 years ago as Lake Otero dried. Today, four basic types of dunes are found at White Sands. Dome dunes develop just downwind of Lake Lucero. Crescent-shaped barchan dunes form where there is a limited supply of sand. Parabolic dunes, also crescent shaped, form when vegetation anchors the tips of the crescent. Where there is plentiful sand, long ridges known as transverse dunes develop. Blowouts, depressions in the surface caused by the removal of sand, are also frequently seen. Sometimes, pillars of sand anchored by vegetation will remain in the center of blowouts. The gypsum makes these dunes look bright white under the desert sun, whereas most dunes are made of tan quartz sand and thus are not so bright. The dune ecosystem at White Sands is still active, with some dunes moving more than 300 feet in a single year, making each visit to White Sands just a little bit different.

Estimated area of Lake Otero at its maximum size in Pleistocene time compared to that of the modern ephemeral Lake Lucero. The gypsum dunes are protected at White Sands National Park. The visitor center is located about 16 miles west of Alamogordo on US 70.

Vegetation stabilizing a pillar of sand in a blowout.

Four main types of dunes occur at White Sands depending on the supply of sand and the amount of vegetation in the area. —Modified from *Roadside Geology of Colorado*, Third Edition, 2014

Wind creates ripples in the sand. —Photograph courtesy National Park Service

Dome dunes are small and circular. They are fast moving and form at the southwest margin of the White Sands dune field, near the edge of Lake Lucero.

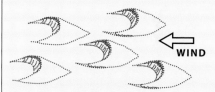

Barchan dunes are thickest in their middle. They form when wind blows sparse sand in one direction across a flat surface. These and transverse dunes dominate the White Sands dune field and are found at its center.

Transverse dunes, with long, gentle windward slopes, form when sand is abundant, wind blows from one direction, and there are few plants. These and barchan dunes are most abundant at White Sands dune field and are found primarily at its center.

Parabolic dunes develop when vegetation anchors a dune's curved arms while the wind blows away sand at its center. These slow-moving dunes are found along the northern, southern, and northeastern margins of the White Sands dune field.

Dripping Springs Natural Area in the Organ Mountains

Thunderous Eruptions Followed by Resonating Solitude

Rising to about 9,000 feet in elevation east of Las Cruces, the Organ Mountains look unlike any other mountains in New Mexico. The towering, rounded spires of the Needles Section are said to resemble the pipes of an organ in a great cathedral, giving the mountains their name. The spire rocks are monzonite, an igneous rock similar to granite but containing less quartz. Around 36 million years ago, this rock was a magma chamber almost 2 miles underground. It provided the magma for explosive caldera-forming supervolcano eruptions that created three ash-flow tuffs that covered the region.

From 15 to 8 million years ago, when the Rio Grande Rift was actively splitting this region apart, these fault-block mountains were uplifted, and the monzonite that was once underground was exposed at the surface. The organ-pipe shape developed from the weathering of joints in the rock. When rocks that originally formed deep underground under a lot of pressure are later exposed at Earth's surface, the pressure exerted on the rocks is much less, so they expand. Cracks, called sheet joints, open up, and the rock weathers into a rounded shape.

Some early Spanish maps named these mountains La Sierra de la Soledad, or the Mountains of Solitude, a fitting name. Many lonely places lie deep amidst narrow canyons cut through the rugged rocks. At Dripping Springs Natural Area, the cliffs on either side of the deep canyon are ash-flow tuff from the supervolcano eruption 36 million years ago. At Dripping Springs, also known as the Weeping Wall, water trickles downward through a narrow slot canyon from high in the mountains.

In the late 1800s, this quiet canyon of beauty became a popular place for people from Las Cruces to escape the heat of the Rio Grande valley. A two-story resort hotel was built, which later was converted to a sanatorium for tuberculosis patients. A rancher eventually acquired the property and used it for grazing and water rights. Today, the cattle are gone, the resort and sanatorium structures are gradually deteriorating, and solitude is slowly returning to the canyon and its weeping wall.

The stone-walled basin was built to catch water from the Weeping Wall to supply the resort once located at Dripping Springs.

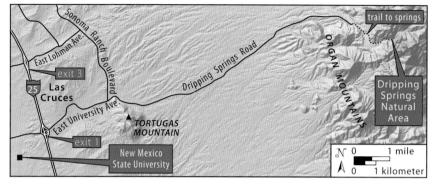

To get to Dripping Springs Natural Area, take exit 1 from I-25 and head east on East University Avenue. After a few curves, this will become Dripping Springs Road, which ends at the parking lot for the natural area. A 1.5-mile-long trail leads to the Weeping Wall.

Weathering of the igneous rocks that make up the Organ Mountains gives them a profile unlike that of other uplifts along the Rio Grande Rift.

Numerous fossil tracks have been discovered in these red Permian-aged rocks.

Prehistoric Trackways National Monument
THE LAND BEFORE DINOSAURS

Northwest of Las Cruces, the Robledo Mountains look like many other mountains in the Chihuahuan Desert—rugged rocks dotted with creosote, yucca, ocotillo, and other cacti. These reddish rocks, however, are a window into the world that existed in the Permian Period, when all continents were stuck together as a single supercontinent known as Pangea. New Mexico was located at the western coast of Pangea near the equator. The rocks in Prehistoric Trackways National Monument, the Hueco Group, were deposited in rivers, floodplains, tidal flats, and the warm shallow sea at the edge of the giant continent. Brachiopods, bryozoans, crinoids, sponges, corals, snails, and ammonites are common in some of the marine limestones. Petrified logs are also sometimes found. Floods from ancient storms washed these into the ocean, where they were buried and preserved in the seafloor sediment.

On the coastal plain, a tropical forest was home to many animals that left their tracks in the mud of tidal flats and river floodplains. Some were created by insects, other arthropods, crustaceans, and amphibians. In addition to tracks, burrows show where organisms dug into the sediment searching for food or shelter. In some places, body impressions show where animals rested on soft mud. Some of the most interesting tracks were left by the reptile *Dimetrodon*, a major predator of the time. While often mistaken for a dinosaur, *Dimetrodon* is a synapsid, or mammal-like reptile. (Dinosaurs would not enter the scene until the Triassic Period, which follows the Permian.) The preserved tracks of *Dimetrodon* and other organisms allow paleontologists to see how these animals moved and interacted with each other.

More than 2,500 slabs of tracks have been recovered for study, making this location one of the finest assemblages of Permian trackways and other trace fossils in the world. Most of these slabs have been removed from the site for study but can be seen at the New Mexico Museum of Natural History and Science in Albuquerque.

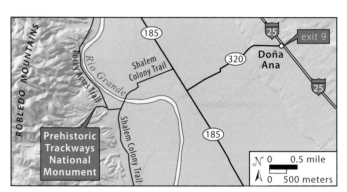

To reach Prehistoric Trackways National Monument, leave I-25 at Doña Ana (exit 9) and take NM 320 west to NM 185. Turn right and drive for about 0.5 mile, then turn left on Shalem Colony Trail. Drive about 1.5 miles, cross the Rio Grande, and turn right onto Rocky Acres Trail. Go approximately 0.25 mile and bear left onto the only dirt road that goes west, Permian Track Road.

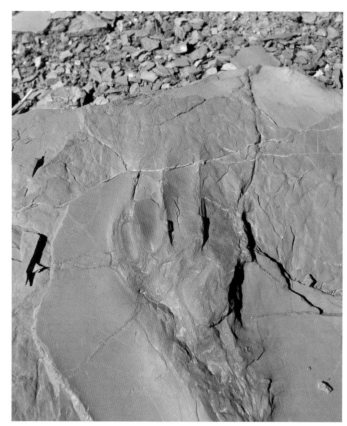

A Dimetrodon *track discovered at the national monument.*
—Photograph by Bob Wick, Bureau of Land Management

Dimetrodon *was a major predator of the Permian when the area around Prehistoric Trackways National Monument was a tropical forest at the edge of the sea.* —Illustration by Tama Higuchi

39

Kilbourne Hole
A MAAR VOLCANO DELIVERS PIECES OF THE MANTLE

The barren desert west of El Paso, Texas, was volcanically active as recently as 20,000 years ago as the Potrillo volcanic field. Numerous cinder cones and lava flows grace the youthful landscape, and in New Mexico you can drive to Kilbourne Hole, a real novelty in the volcanic world. Kilbourne Hole, an oval-shaped crater approximately 1.7 miles long, 1 mile wide, and about 300 feet deep, is a maar volcano. This type of volcano forms when hot magma hits shallow groundwater. The water flash boils into steam and blasts a crater, or maar, in the ground. The eruption cut through the 81,000- to 70,000-year-old Afton basalt flows, indicating that the maar is younger. Surrounding the crater are pale-colored base-surge deposits that form when there is more steam and gas in an eruption than ash and other pyroclastic material. A base surge contains small spherical pellets, called accretionary lapilli, that form as fine-grained ash particles stick together around condensing water droplets or solid particles. Surge deposits typically have cross beds and reverse graded beds, both of which can be seen around the crater.

Kilbourne Hole is best known for volcanic bombs and xenoliths. A volcanic bomb forms when lava explodes from a volcano. As the molten blob flies through the air, it cools into an aerodynamic teardrop shape. Many of the volcanic bombs at Kilbourne Hole contain xenoliths, which are pieces of rock picked up by magma as it rises to the surface. The magma that erupted at Kilbourne Hole originated about 40 miles underground, allowing it to pick up pieces of the lower crust and upper mantle. These rocks from deep in the Earth provide geologists with samples they would otherwise never obtain. Some of the xenoliths are also beautiful, especially those that are peridotite from the mantle, which contains the dark-green mineral olivine. Occasionally gem-quality olivine, known as peridot, is found in the xenoliths.

This peridotite xenolith contains abundant green olivine crystals, a mineral that is common in Earth's mantle but rare at the surface. The xenolith is surrounded by dark basaltic lava.

The small circular pellets in the base-surge deposits surrounding Kilbourne Hole are called accretionary lapilli.

Kilbourne Hole, located in Organ Mountains–Desert Peaks National Monument, is off the beaten path on good dirt roads. Take exit 155 from I-10 at Vado Drive. Head west to the stop sign at NM 478 and turn left. After approximately 0.2 mile, turn right on NM 189 and travel approximately 1.1 miles to NM 28. Turn left and drive south for approximately 2 miles. Turn right on West Afton Road. After driving about 11.2 miles, turn left on Douglas Munro Road and drive approximately 6.5 miles. At the T in the roadway, turn left and drive approximately 0.2 mile, crossing the railroad tracks. Turn left on County Road A017. After driving approximately 7.2 miles, turn right on County Road A011. Drive about 8.1 miles to the crater. The southeast corner of the crater is located at 31° 57′ 25″ N, 106° 57′ 22″ W.

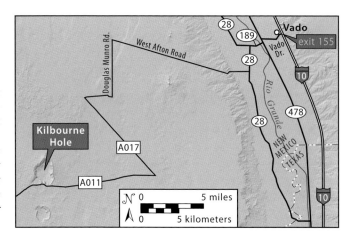

Kilbourne Hole, a large maar volcano, erupted through a flat basalt plain. Note the black line of basalt around the crater rim.

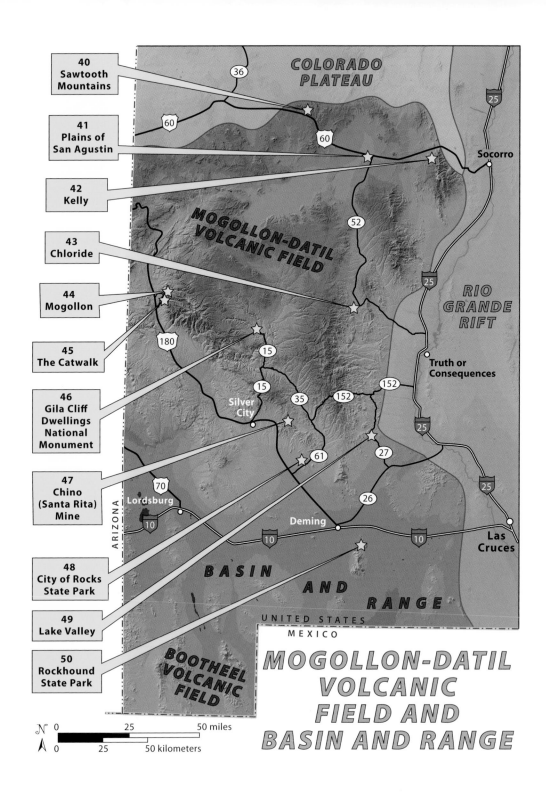

40
Sawtooth Mountains

41
Plains of San Agustin

42
Kelly

43
Chloride

44
Mogollon

45
The Catwalk

46
Gila Cliff Dwellings National Monument

47
Chino (Santa Rita) Mine

48
City of Rocks State Park

49
Lake Valley

50
Rockhound State Park

COLORADO PLATEAU

Socorro

MOGOLLON-DATIL VOLCANIC FIELD

RIO GRANDE RIFT

Truth or Consequences

Silver City

ARIZONA

Lordsburg

Deming

Las Cruces

UNITED STATES
MEXICO

BASIN AND RANGE

BOOTHEEL VOLCANIC FIELD

N
0   25   50 miles
0   25   50 kilometers

MOGOLLON-DATIL VOLCANIC FIELD AND BASIN AND RANGE

During the Mid-Tertiary ignimbrite flare-up, caldera-forming volcanic eruptions created numerous volcanic fields from the Sierra Madre Occidental in Mexico northward into New Mexico, Colorado, Utah, and even Nevada. During explosive eruptions, pyroclastic flows—fast-moving masses of hot ash, gases, and volcanic fragments—blanketed the landscape, solidifying as ash-flow tuffs (ignimbrites). In the Mogollon-Datil volcanic field of west-central New Mexico, volcanism began with basaltic andesite and rhyolite eruptions from about 40 million years ago to 36 million years ago. These continued until about 24 million years ago, creating a landscape of lava flows, ash-flow tuffs, volcanic domes, and calderas. The southwest corner of the state features the Bootheel volcanic field, which contains nine calderas, with eight in or at least partially in New Mexico. They erupted between 36 and 26 million years ago. Erosion and faulting during the succeeding years made these ancient calderas much more difficult to identify than New Mexico's younger volcanoes, such as the young Valles caldera (site 17) that formed only 1.25 million years ago. Hot fluids circulating through the rocks following the volcanic activity are responsible for numerous mineral deposits in the region, making this area home to many of New Mexico's frontier boomtowns.

Some of the volcanic rocks have been exposed by normal faulting in the Basin and Range Province, which covers a large area of the western United States, including most of Nevada and parts of Utah, Idaho, California, Arizona, Texas, and New Mexico. This region is characterized by a series of rugged north-trending mountain ranges separated by arid valleys. This unique pattern of topography began forming about 20 million years ago as tectonic forces pulled the crust of the region apart. Normal faults developed to accommodate these tensional forces. Blocks of crust that were dropped down along faults became the basins, and the adjacent uplifted blocks became the mountain ranges.

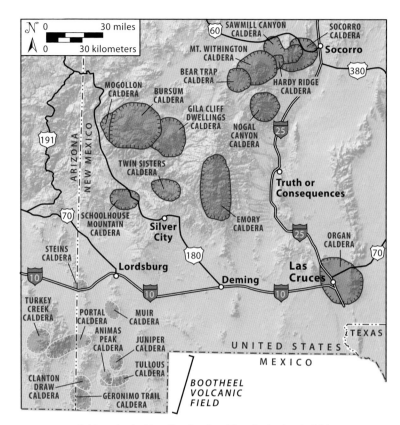

Calderas in the Mogollon-Datil and Bootheel volcanic fields.

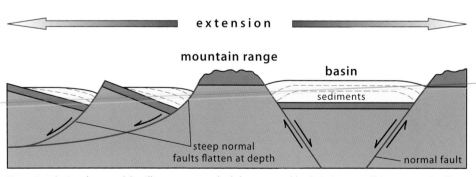

Extension during the past 20 million years stretched the crust and broke it into parallel ranges and valleys.

The Sawtooth Mountains form the jagged skyline in a remote part of western New Mexico. The rocks that form these mountains are the Dog Springs Formation, which is composed mostly of volcanic debris eroded from the Mogollon-Datil volcanic field and deposited around 37 million years ago. The lower part of the formation was deposited by rivers flowing northward from the volcanic field. The upper part of the formation is predominantly debris flow breccia containing abundant andesite and dacite clasts, as well as large fragments of Pennsylvanian limestone. A debris flow is a thick, water-saturated mass of rock fragments and sediment that moves rapidly downslope. This landslide raced down hillsides from a volcanic center south of Datil, carrying mostly volcanic debris from its source area but also picking up eroded pieces of older rocks, such as the limestone, along the way.

Near Monument Rock, an erosional pillar of the Dog Springs Formation, one can see evidence of an ancient earthquake in the form of highly contorted sedimentary layers. This type of irregularity, called soft-sediment deformation, occurred during an earthquake while the sediment was still unconsolidated and saturated with water. The shaking caused the sediment particles to separate, allowing water to flow between them, and for a while the sediment acted like a liquid. The contorted layers in the Dog Springs Formation, now lithified into solid rock, record an earthquake that rocked New Mexico in the Eocene Epoch.

Monument Rock, a prominent landmark in the Sawtooth Mountains.

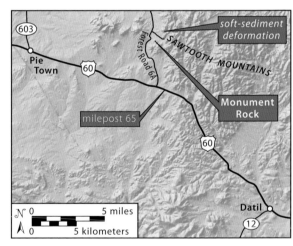

To get to the Sawtooth Mountains, take US 60 west for 12.3 miles from Datil. Turn north on Forest Road 6A. After driving about 4 miles, a double-track leads to the east. At this point you will see Monument Rock on the right, and the soft-sediment deformation can be seen in the mountains on both sides of the forest road. The best outcrops of the soft-sediment deformation are visible along the double-track to the right, but a four-wheel-drive vehicle with high clearance is recommended for this.

Close-up of the soft-sediment deformation caused by the Eocene Epoch earthquake.

The Dog Springs Formation includes undeformed beds overlying beds with soft-sediment deformation.

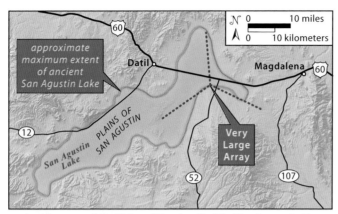

Location map of the Plains of San Agustin. The blue line marks the approximate maximum extent of the lake that occupied the Plains of San Agustin during the last ice age

The radio telescope antenna used at the VLA are 82 feet in diameter and weigh 230 tons.

41 Plains of San Agustin
LOOKING INTO THE COSMOS FROM AN ANCIENT LAKE

Following the intense volcanism that created the Mogollon-Datil volcanic field, tensional stress pulled apart the area now occupied by the Plains of San Agustin. This created three distinct grabens, or down-dropped fault blocks, the deepest of which might have been displaced as much as 4,000 feet along normal faults. Over time, sediment filled these basins, creating today's broad, flat topography, a vast expanse of grassland with grazing cattle, pronghorn, and the occasional elk. Surrounding the plains are numerous low hills, many of which are small volcanic vents.

During the Pleistocene ice ages, New Mexico's climate was much cooler and wetter. While glaciers covered much of northern North America 20,000 years ago, a lake as much as 250 feet deep and covering about 450 square miles occupied the San Agustin Basin. In some places, you can see ancient shorelines of this lake.

After the climate became warmer and drier at the end of the ice ages, grasslands colonized the former lakebed. Between 1885 and the early 1970s, ranchers drove cattle and sheep across the grasslands to the railhead in Magdalena. The trail across the wide plain became known as the Magdalena Stock Driveway. Wells drilled into the aquifer of the ancient lake sediments provided water along the way.

In the 1970s, the Plains of San Agustin were chosen as the site of the Very Large Array (VLA) radio telescope. The flat topography, dry climate, high elevation, and remote location are perfect for recording the radio emissions of distant celestial objects. Many parts of the universe radiate wavelengths in the electromagnetic spectrum, which includes types of light not visible to humans. Radio telescopes record these signals and convert the data into visible images. Twenty-seven radio telescope antenna dishes occupy the ancient lake basin. Rail lines are used to place them in different configurations so they can expand our knowledge of distant corners of the universe. A visitor center at the VLA includes exhibits about radio astronomy and information about current research.

Once covered with as much as 250 feet of water, the lake bottom is now a vast, flat grassland.

Kelly
A WORLD-FAMOUS MINERAL LOCALITY

In 1866, Civil War veteran Colonel J. S. Hutchason discovered limestone altered with numerous colorful minerals at the northern edge of the Magdalena Mountains. He staked the first claims of what would become Kelly. Mining remained small-scale until the mid-1870s, when investors purchased shares of the mining claims and expanded operations. In 1883, a post office was established, and by the beginning of the twentieth century the population had grown to about 3,000 as Kelly became a leading producer of zinc and lead in New Mexico. When production declined after World War I, so did the population, and in 1945 the post office closed. This once-thriving mining town has been reduced mostly to ruins, foundations, and piles of mining waste rock.

Kelly is on private property, so obtain permission to visit from Tony's Rock Shop in Magdalena. Magdalena Peak, a rhyolite dome that erupted around 13 million years ago, is to the

southwest of Magdalena. Talus, fallen blocks of rock created by weathering and erosion, accumulated on the side of the mountain forming the shape of a woman's face in profile. Early Spanish explorers, recalling a legend in Spain of St. Mary Magdalene's visage appearing on a mountainside, named this mountain La Sierra de Maria Magdalena.

From Magdalena, take Kelly Road to a Y junction where the road passes some odd-looking cement structures that were part of the mill for the Graphic Mine, built in 1917. Keep left at the Y to continue to Kelly. The road passes St. John the Baptist Catholic Church on the right, the only building from the mining days still maintained. Mass is celebrated here on certain feast days and fiestas. Not far beyond the church is the location of the famous Kelly Mine. The most prominent structure remaining is the steel headframe that was designed by Alexander G. Eiffel

Looking down at the Kelly Mine site. The tall brick-and-concrete structure is the ruins of the Tri-Bullion smelter. The black steel headframe sits above the Kelly Mine. The mountain in the background is Magdalena Peak.

(of Eiffel Tower fame) for the Carnegie Steelworks. It was purchased as a kit from Traylor Engineering Company and erected in 1906. Near the headframe are brick remains of the Tri-Bullion smelter. You can see waste rock piles of many other important mines in the district, including the Juanita and the Germany, in the surrounding hills.

The ore deposits at Kelly were formed when magma intruded Paleozoic limestone in the late Oligocene Epoch. Hot water related to these igneous intrusions followed fractures and layers in the rock, especially porous parts of the Kelly Limestone known as the Silver Pipe. This hot, mineral-rich water reacted with the host rock, creating the primary ore minerals sphalerite, galena, chalcopyrite, and pyrite. In addition, the heat of the magma metamorphosed adjacent rocks and altered them, creating minerals such as andradite, grossular garnet, hedenbergite, diopside, and wollastonite. Later, groundwater percolating through the rocks oxidized parts of the ore deposit, creating additional valuable minerals, including smithsonite, cerrusite, anglesite, hydrozincite, malachite, and azurite.

The mines at Kelly primarily produced lead and zinc, but copper, silver, and gold were also extracted. Among mineral collectors, light-blue smithsonite from Kelly is world-famous and highly prized. It and other interesting minerals can still be found on the piles of rock surrounding the old mines.

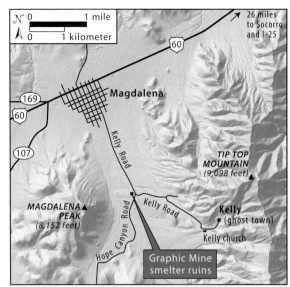

Kelly is private property and permission to visit must be obtained from Tony's Rock Shop in Magdalena.

Light-blue smithsonite, highly desired today by collectors around the world, was mined for its zinc content.

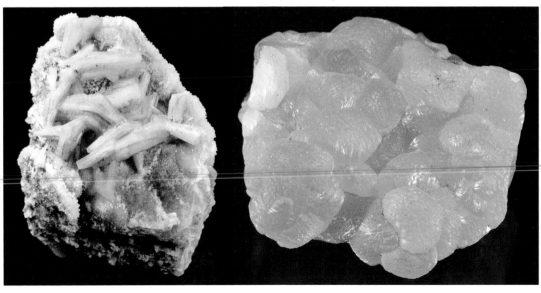

The mines around Kelly produced many interesting specimens, such as this yellow barite (also spelled baryte) on white druzy quartz from the Juanita Mine.

97

While working as a freighter for the US Army, Harry Pye hauled supplies from Hillsboro to Camp Ojo Caliente in southern Socorro County. In a canyon at the edge of the Black Range, he discovered rocks rich in chlorargyrite (silver chloride). When his contract with the army was done in 1879, he returned to the canyon and staked mining claims. Only a few months later, Apaches killed Pye, but word of his rich silver strike was out, and miners raced to the area.

The bedrock that hosts the ore is mostly andesite, dacite, and rhyolite volcanics erupted from the Mogollon-Datil volcanic field during the Mid-Tertiary ignimbrite flare-up. About 29 to 27 million years ago, hot water from a magma chamber flowed through fractures and faults in the rocks, depositing veins that not only contain silver minerals but also minerals rich in copper, gold, lead, and sometimes zinc. The largest vein system, known as the Great Master Lode, assayed a rich 50 to 60 ounces of gold per ton and more than 200 ounces of silver per ton during the glory days of mining in the 1880s.

Chloride, named for the rich silver chloride ore, has a history similar to that of many mining towns of the West. News of a discovery spread quickly after Pye staked his claims, and by 1880 a tent city existed. By 1881, stagecoach service and a post office had been established, and more permanent structures were built. The late 1880s were the glory days for Chloride as it grew into a town with a newspaper, mercantile stores, livery stables, a candy store, a drug store, a hotel, a photographer's studio, and other typical businesses of a thriving mining community. The town, however, lacked reputable single women, so property in town was offered to single women who moved to Chloride.

An oversupply of silver followed by its devaluation and the Panic of 1893 caused the silver mines to close, leaving Chloride and other silver-mining towns mere shadows of their booming past. Today, several restored buildings from the mining boom can be visited in Chloride, including a former dance hall and saloon, as well as a general store. When the Pioneer Store closed in 1923, the owners boarded the windows but left all the furniture and merchandise inside with the intent to eventually reopen the business. It was never reopened, and in the 1990s the store and all its inventory were restored, allowing visitors to step into a time capsule of a frontier mining town.

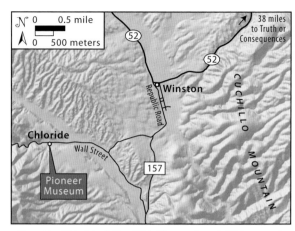

To get to Chloride, follow NM 52 west from I-25 just north of Truth or Consequences. In Winston, turn left on Republic Road. After about 2.7 miles, the road comes to a T. Turn right onto Wall Street, which is the main road through Chloride.

Chrysocolla (greenish-blue copper mineral) and quartz (clear) found at the Silver Monument Mine in the Chloride mining district. At the lower-left center there is a 3-millimeter-long rope of silver. Silver wires in the upper-right center are mostly obscured by the greenish chrysocolla. —Photograph by Don Saathoff

Looking down Wall Street, the main street of Chloride. The Pioneer Store and the Monte Cristo Saloon and Dance Hall are on the right. Rocks of the Rubio Peak Formation that were deposited in volcanic debris flows are exposed in the background. The richest mines in the Chloride district were in the hills behind those rocks.

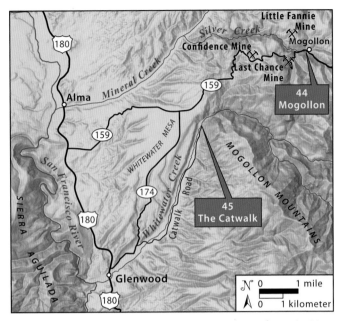

To get to Mogollon, take NM 159 (Bursum Road) east from US 180 just south of Alma. To get to the Catwalk (site 45), turn east onto NM 174 from US 180 in Glenwood. After about 1 mile, turn right onto Catwalk Road and follow it to the recreation area.

Mogollon
VEINS WITH GOLD AND SILVER

About 28 million years ago, the area around Mogollon was rocked by a massive volcanic eruption that formed the Bursum caldera. Following the eruption, hot water related to this volcanic activity flowed through cracks in the rocks and precipitated ore minerals in veins close to Earth's surface. At Mogollon, these veins were enriched in gold and silver.

In 1874, Sergeant James Cooney of the 8th US Cavalry discovered some of these veins. When he left of the army the following year, he staked the first mining claims in what would become the Mogollon mining district. The early years of Mogollon were difficult with frequent Apache raids, a fire that nearly destroyed the entire town, and flash floods. By the early 1900s, the population had grown to more than two thousand, and the town boasted such modern luxuries as electricity, telephones, and a movie theater. At the end of World War I, metal prices dropped, and by 1924 the mines closed. Activity resumed in 1937, and operations continued through World War II. The last mine closed in 1952.

The mountainous drive to Mogollon on NM 159 follows a steep, narrow, curving road that convicts built in 1897. It offers spectacular views of the Mogollon-Datil volcanic field, as well as some of the mine sites. Look to the north across a canyon just west of town to see the prominent white tailings of the Little Fannie Mine, the last mine to operate in the district. At a hairpin curve just outside the town, the road passes close to the reddish metal ruins of the Last Chance Mine, a major producer of both gold and silver. From there, it is a short distance to Mogollon, located at the bottom of Silver Creek Canyon.

Ruins of the Little Fannie Mine, the last mine to close in Mogollon, cling to the mountain just outside town.

The Catwalk in Whitewater Canyon
BRINGING WATER TO A MINING MILL

45

Whitewater Canyon is a steep-sided, narrow slot canyon carved into the 34-million-year-old Cooney Tuff. This rock was erupted as a pyroclastic flow from the Mogollon caldera, one of the many caldera-forming eruptions that created the Mogollon-Datil volcanic field. The Catwalk National Recreation Trail that winds through the canyon traces its history back to 1893, when mines were extracting gold and silver from veins in the rock. John T. Graham, superintendent of the Confidence Mine, selected the mouth of Whitewater Canyon as the location for the mine's stamp mill, which crushed the rock to release the ore, as well as for the mill's settlers and concentrators. Due to the narrowness of the canyon, the mill could not be constructed any closer to the mine. The site did not always have enough water for the mill, so a steady supply of water was brought from higher in the mountains through the canyon in large pipes fastened to the steep rock walls. Workers who maintained the pipeline dubbed it the Catwalk.

The mill closed in 1913, but the Catwalk was revived in 1935 when workers from the Civilian Conservation Corps built a scenic hiking trail that followed the old pipeline. The parking lot for the trail was the site of Graham (also known as Whitewater), a small town that served the mill. Ruins of the mill can be seen on the hillside west of the parking lot.

Flash floods are a serious hazard at Whitewater Canyon. During the monsoon season from July to October, cloudbursts sometimes drop several inches of rain over the Mogollon Mountains. The impermeable rocks and steep slopes mean most of the water becomes runoff that enters the canyon. One of these flash floods occurred in 2013 when 10 inches of rain fell on the night of September 14, resulting in a 20-foot-wall of water roaring through the canyon with a maximum discharge of 16,100 cubic feet per second, six times higher than any flow previously observed. The metal catwalk, picnic area, and parking lot were all damaged or destroyed; however, it is events like this that also helped create and shape the canyon. The first half mile of the trail has since been restored.

The metal walkway of the Catwalk is secured to the hard Cooney Tuff above the water flowing through Whitewater Canyon.

101

The Gila Cliff Dwellings are hidden in alcoves eroded into the Gila Conglomerate.

Gila Cliff Dwellings National Monument
A VILLAGE HIDDEN IN THE MOUNTAINS

46

Around AD 1280, the Mogollon people traveled from the area around Reserve, New Mexico, southeast into the rugged mountains, where they built new homes in a remote canyon. No one knows why they undertook this arduous journey, but the homes they built are preserved in the Gila Cliff Dwellings National Monument north of Silver City.

The national monument is in the Mogollon-Datil volcanic field on the eastern edge of the Gila Cliff Dwellings caldera, which formed 28 million years ago in a colossal volcanic eruption. Not long after, an even more cataclysmic eruption formed the Bursum caldera. This destroyed the western portion of the Gila Cliff Dwellings caldera and covered much of the landscape with the Bloodgood Canyon Tuff, an ash flow. After a few million years of quiescence, volcanic activity resumed with the eruption of basalt and andesite lava flows. After the volcanic activity ended, pull-apart forces related to the Basin and

Range created the Gila Hot Springs graben, a block of crust that dropped downward along normal faults. The highlands surrounding the graben eroded and filled it with volcanic-rich sediments, including the Gila Conglomerate that hosts the cliff dwellings.

All this rich geologic history can be seen along a hiking trail leading to the cliff dwellings. On the north side of the parking lot at the trailhead are pale-colored rocks of the Bloodgood Canyon Tuff. While it is as much as 600 feet thick in places, only the uppermost part of it is seen here. Looking closely at the tuff, you can see pumice fragments, ash particles, and crystals of different minerals. The most striking of these crystals is sanidine, a type of feldspar that reflects light with a bluish glow, which is why it is also called moonstone.

Above the tuff are the basalt and andesite lava flows that erupted 27 to 24 million years ago. These flows also contain

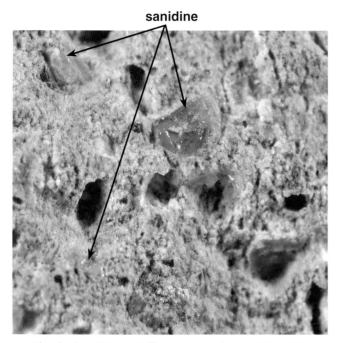

sanidine

The Bloodgood Canyon Tuff contains abundant sanidine, which sometimes glows blue in sunlight.

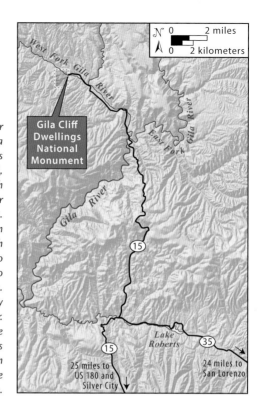

To get to the visitor center of the Gila Cliff Dwellings National Monument, follow NM 15 north from Silver City for just over 45 miles. Alternately, you can take NM 35 north from San Lorenzo to NM 15 and on to the cliff dwellings. This route is only about 1 mile longer. Be sure you arrive at the cliff dwellings before 4 p.m., when the trail to the site closes.

White quartz, calcite, and zeolites fill vesicles of the lava flows that overlie the Bloodgood Canyon Tuff. Pocket knife for scale.

The Mogollon people traveled through rugged mountains to find a place to build their homes. This view of the eroded volcanic landscape was taken from NM 15, looking west toward Alum Mountain.

interesting details worth a close-up examination. When lava erupts, the volcanic gases it contains bubble up and can be trapped as the lava solidifies. These open spaces, called vesicles, are sometimes later filled with minerals deposited by water flowing through the rock. Look closely at the mineral-filled vesicles in these lava flows to see crystals of quartz, calcite, and zeolites.

Overlying the lava flows is the Gila Conglomerate, the thick sequence of conglomerate, with some sandstone and shale, that filled the Gila Hot Springs graben. While hot springs cannot be seen on the hike to the cliff dwellings, several are present in the area. Groundwater that has been heated deep underground rises along the faults at the edge of the graben and emerges at springs that are 90 to 150 degrees Fahrenheit.

The Mogollon people who settled in the mountains built their homes from blocks of the Gila Conglomerate in natural alcoves 200 feet above the floor of Cliff Dweller Creek. These alcoves formed at creek level about 500,000 years ago, before the creek cut down to its present elevation. The creek carved away a more easily eroded bed within the conglomerate. Groundwater—forced to exit the conglomerate by an impermeable layer beneath it—enlarged the alcoves. The water slowly dissolved the cement holding the rock together and gradually eroded material away in a process called spring sapping.

About forty masonry rooms were constructed by the Mogollon people to house ten to fifteen families, estimated to be a total of around sixty people. They supplemented the corn, beans, and squash that they grew with hunting in the mountains. The cliff dwellings were only occupied for a few generations. By 1350, a drought forced the families to abandon their homes. They likely moved into the Rio Grande valley, where there was permanent water.

Chino (Santa Rita) Mine
COPPER CONCENTRATED BY GROUNDWATER

While the Rocky Mountains were rising in Colorado, shallow igneous intrusions related to that mountain building event were forming in southern New Mexico and Arizona. One of these bodies of liquid hot magma became the granodiorite of the Santa Rita stock east of Silver City. This magma rose toward Earth's surface about 58 million years ago until it was only a few miles deep. As it cooled and solidified, steam and other gases in the remaining magma built up pressure until it fractured the already solidified rock of the stock and the surrounding country rock. Hot fluids then flowed into the cracks, depositing minerals bearing copper, gold, silver, molybdenum, and platinum group elements, as well as abundant pyrite.

Had the story ended there, we would not be discussing the mineral deposits today because it would not have been economic to mine them. Fortunately, groundwater migrating downward from the surface leached some of the copper from the rocks and concentrated it in an enriched zone containing the copper sulfide mineral chalcocite, as well as other ore minerals, including chrysocolla, malachite, azurite, native copper, and covellite. This interaction between the original minerals and groundwater, known as supergene enrichment, created one of New Mexico's most economic mineral deposits.

Before the first Europeans set foot on North America, Native Americans collected copper and other minerals from the area. Around 1800, an Apache showed this location to a Spanish military officer. Lacking the finances to develop the mineral deposit, the officer sold the claim to a businessman in Mexico

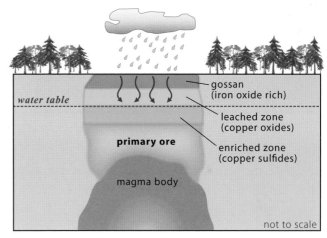

Groundwater leaches metals from a mineral deposit and concentrates them at the water table creating an oxidized zone and an enriched zone of ore minerals. A weathered zone at the surface, called gossan, contains only iron oxides, not ore minerals.

who obtained permission from Spain to establish a mine using convict labor. Mining was abandoned around 1840 due to political unrest and the threat of Apache attack. After the American Civil War, mining in the area resumed, with many of the miners living in the town of Santa Rita. Once the highest-grade ore was depleted by underground mining, open-pit mining began in 1910 to exploit the lower-grade ore around the Santa Rita stock. As mining expanded, the town of Santa Rita was abandoned, and its original location is now floating in the open space of the massive mining pit.

A locally famous rock formation, known as the Kneeling Nun, is found at the east side of the Chino Mine. This eroded

The best place to view both the large mining pit of the Chino Mine and the Kneeling Nun is along NM 152 east of Hanover.

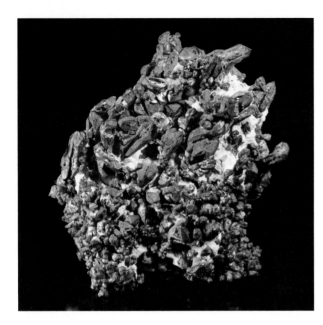

A sample of native copper from the Chino Mine.

Open-pit mining began in 1910. —Photograph by Frank Karasti

column of rock has taken the shape of a devout woman kneeling in prayer before an altar. The Kneeling Nun Tuff, a major rock unit that was violently erupted from the Emory caldera about 34.9 million years ago and covered the surrounding area with hot volcanic debris, was named for the column. As the volcanic material cooled, it contracted, and large cracks, called joints, formed. Weathering and erosion were concentrated along these fractures, creating the shape of the kneeling nun. Early Spanish settlers of the area told the tale of a young nun who fell in love with a soldier and was banished from her order for it. Grieving for lost love, and in penance for her sins, she climbed the mountain to pray, and her pious figure was forever preserved in the rock.

The Kneeling Nun at the edge of the Chino open pit, viewed from NM 152 east of Hanover.

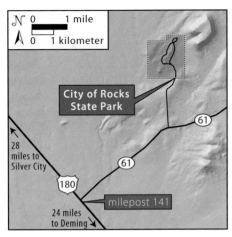

City of Rocks State Park is located between Deming and Silver City. To get there, take NM 61 east from US 180. Drive approximately 3 miles and look for the entrance to the park on the left.

City of Rocks State Park
PINNACLES OF JOINTED RHYOLITE TUFF

Spires, pinnacles, and bulbous columns of pale rock rising out of the desert, seemingly along a grid of streets and avenues, greet visitors to City of Rocks State Park in the Mimbres Valley. The landforms trace their origins to 34.9 million years ago when a massive eruption of rhyolite exploded from the Emory caldera to the east. This explosion produced pyroclastic flows of very hot volcanic gas, pumice, ash, and other volcanic debris that raced from the caldera across the surrounding landscape. The material in the pyroclastic flow was still extremely hot when it covered the land, so it fused together as a hard rock now called the Kneeling Nun Tuff. Within this rhyolite tuff are visible crystals surrounded by a pale matrix of microscopic minerals, ash, and volcanic glass fragments. Common crystals that you can see with the naked eye include glassy quartz and sanidine, blocky black hornblende, and platy bits of biotite that often have a bronze luster.

The "streets" and "avenues" between the columns of rock initially were a series of joints that formed as the rock cooled and contracted. Other joints formed during pressure release as the overlying rock that had buried the Kneeling Nun Tuff was eroded away. Frost wedging, root wedging, water flow, and wind enlarged these cracks over the years. Some weathering even occurred while the rocks were still buried as humic acids from decaying vegetation in the soil weakened the rock. The resulting labyrinth is home to numerous animals, including scorpions, snakes, small mammals, and several species of birds.

The Kneeling Nun Tuff includes numerous visible and microscopic minerals.

Weathering and erosion are concentrated along fractures in the rocks, creating many unique shapes.

City of Rocks rises out of the Mimbres Valley floor.

As with many western ghost towns, Lake Valley's early history was not well documented, and today, fact and folklore are intertwined as accepted history. Silver was initially discovered in 1876 by Mr. McEverts, a local rancher, or perhaps it was discovered in 1878 by a cowboy named George Lufkin. Either way, by 1878, a mining camp named Sierra City was established. As more permanent structures were built, the town was renamed Daly City in honor of a mine manager who was killed while fighting Apaches. After the town was destroyed by fire, a new one was built closer to the stamp mills and named Lake Valley after a nearby dry lakebed.

Lake Valley remained just another Western silver-mining town until 1881, when blacksmith John Leavitt uncovered something remarkable while working a mining claim he had leased. Only 40 feet below the surface, he discovered a cave lined with crystals of chlorargyrite (silver chloride) and bromargyrite (silver bromide). Named the Bridal Chamber by miners because of the bright sparkle of the silver-bearing minerals lining the walls, this cavern was about 200-feet-long and about 10-to-20 feet high from floor to ceiling. The thick deposits of silver ore covering every surface in the cave held one of the richest concentrations of silver ever discovered. An estimated 78 tons of silver were extracted from the Bridal Chamber. Samples were sent to the National Mining Exposition at Denver, Colorado, in 1882; the largest was a piece of chlorargyrite weighing 640 pounds. Sadly, no photos exist of this legendary mineral deposit.

The ores at Lake Valley formed due to a perfect sequence of geologic events. About 350 million years ago, early in the Mississippian Period, the Lake Valley Limestone was deposited in a warm, shallow sea. Much later, about 60 to 50 million

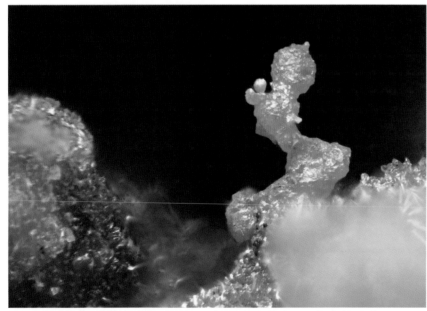

A specimen of chlorargyrite growing on druzy quartz that was collected just above the Bridal Chamber. —Photograph by Frank Karasti

Lake Valley is located 17 miles south of Hillsboro on NM 27.

The stark desert landscape of Lake Valley belied the silver riches hidden just a few feet beneath the surface.

years ago, deformation related to the formation of the Rocky Mountains created faults and fractures in the limestone. Hot, mineral-rich fluids associated with the Mogollon-Datil volcanic field flowed along those faults and fractures, depositing silver minerals, not only along the pathways but also in layers within the limestone, where the silver replaced calcite. Entire beds of limestone can get replaced by ore minerals because calcite is a very chemically reactive mineral. Tectonic activity during the formation of the Rio Grande Rift brought these deposits up close to the land surface, where interactions with groundwater oxidized and concentrated the ore in rich deposits like those in the Bridal Chamber.

An 1895 fire destroyed Lake Valley's main street, but many other structures from the glory days of mining are still standing. The Bureau of Land Management maintains the site and offers a walking tour of the town.

When Rockhound State Park was established in 1966, it was the only state park in the United States that encouraged visitors to collect rocks and minerals. The park lies on the western side of the Little Florida Mountains, named by early Spanish explorers after the colorful flowers that bloom across the desert slopes after a wet period. The mountains, however, also hold multihued treasures of a geologic sort. You can find jasper, onyx, agate, obsidian (also called Apache tears), geodes, thundereggs, and perlite.

These collectible rocks and minerals at Rockhound State Park formed during volcanic activity that began about 33 million years ago and ended about 10 million years later. The Little Florida Mountains consist of andesite, dacite, and rhyolite tuffs and lava flows. Some volcanic-rich sediments, as well as rhyolite domes and dikes, also exist.

Geodes and thundereggs are very similar. Geodes are mineral-lined cavities with a hollow center, and thundereggs are mineral-filled cavities, also called spherulites. They both contain layers of chalcedony, a type of microcrystalline quartz. The layers form through a complex sequence of events, including magmatic cooling processes, multiple pulses of hydrothermal activity related to the volcanism, and groundwater flowing through the rocks. Different temperatures and chemistries of these fluids created the unique geodes and other minerals found in the area. Tiltage thundereggs or geodes are prized finds at Rockhound State Park. Fault movement, or movement in a landslide, that occurred as the minerals were forming is reflected by a tilting in their layers.

The term *thunderegg* comes from the legends of ancient Native Americans of Oregon. They discovered some of these nodules around volcanoes and believed the spirits that inhabited those mountains threw them at each other, creating thunder and lighting.

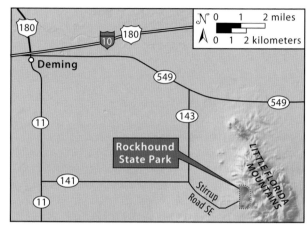

To get to Rockhound State Park, take NM 11 south from Deming. Turn left on NM 141. Continue east on Stirrup Road SE to the entrance of the park.

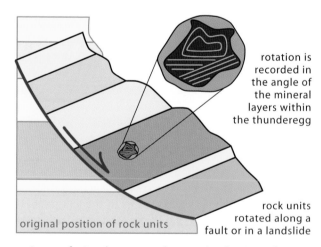

rotation is recorded in the angle of the mineral layers within the thunderegg

original position of rock units

rock units rotated along a fault or in a landslide

Layers of minerals at an angle to each other in a tiltage thunderegg capture movement of the rock along a fault or in a landslide while the minerals were forming.

Jasper, a colorful type of microcrystalline quartz, is one of many minerals commonly found at Rockhound State Park.

Thundereggs are filled with concentric layers of colorful chalcedony. This specimen was found at the nearby Baker Ranch. Although the most accessible sites are a bit picked over at Rockhound State Park, thundereggs can still be found there.

The volcanic rocks of the rugged Little Florida Mountains hide many beautiful thundereggs and geodes.

113

HIGH PLAINS

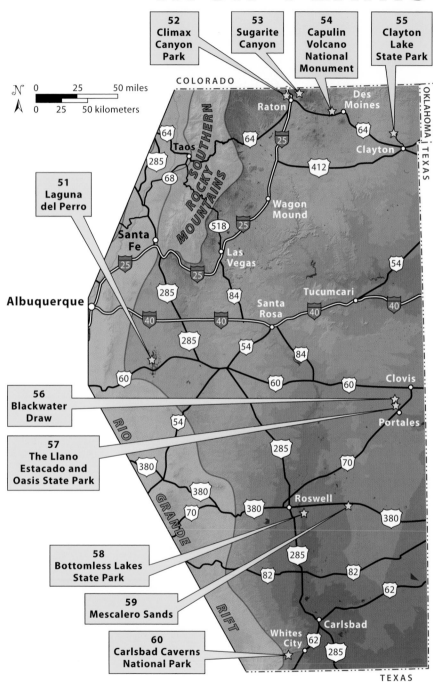

52 Climax Canyon Park

53 Sugarite Canyon

54 Capulin Volcano National Monument

55 Clayton Lake State Park

51 Laguna del Perro

56 Blackwater Draw

57 The Llano Estacado and Oasis State Park

58 Bottomless Lakes State Park

59 Mescalero Sands

60 Carlsbad Caverns National Park

COLORADO

OKLAHOMA | TEXAS

Raton

Des Moines

Clayton

Taos

SOUTHERN ROCKY MOUNTAINS

Wagon Mound

Santa Fe

Las Vegas

Albuquerque

Tucumcari

Santa Rosa

RIO GRANDE RIFT

Clovis

Portales

Roswell

Carlsbad

Whites City

TEXAS

0 25 50 miles
0 25 50 kilometers

While seemingly monotonous and uninteresting, the High Plains of eastern New Mexico include a rich diversity of geology, from young volcanoes and dinosaur trackways in the north to limestone sinkholes and major oil and natural gas deposits in the south. This area was covered by warm, shallow seas several times in the past, the last one retreating around the time of the dinosaur extinction 66 million years ago. As the Rockies rose to the west, erosion in these highlands increased, and rivers carried the sediments eastward, spreading them across the plains. Sand and gravel layers contain groundwater that is used to irrigate crops in this otherwise dry, scarcely populated region. It was not as dry during the Pleistocene ice ages when glaciers covered northern parts of the continent. Toward the end of the last ice age, these plains were home to some of the earliest people to inhabit the Americas. They hunted ancient bison and mammoths that inhabited the lush grasslands.

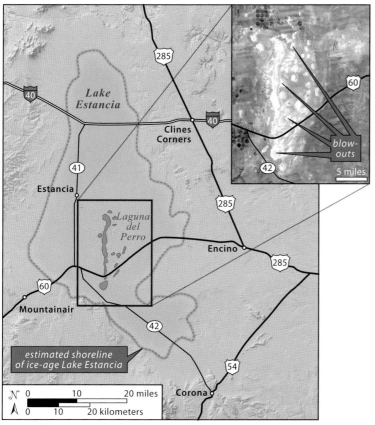

Laguna del Perro and the other blowouts can be seen from US 60, 18 miles east of Mountainair. When the climate was cooler and wetter, Lake Estancia covered about 450 square miles.

51 Laguna del Perro
SALTY BLOWOUTS ON AN ICE-AGE LAKEBED

Today, the area around Laguna del Perro is an arid high desert. From about 25,000 to 12,000 years ago, the climate was cooler and wetter and Lake Estancia covered the region. The exact size of this lake varied, but at its maximum extent it was about 150 feet deep and spread across 450 square miles. As the ice age drew to an end, the region dried and the lake disappeared.

Starting about 700 years ago, wind scoured sediment from the ancient lakebed and created depressions called blowouts. They range from 20 to 40 feet deep. The sediment was deposited nearby as dunes called lunettes. Around eighty-five blowouts and associated lunettes dot the former lakebed, of which Laguna del Perro is the largest at 12 miles long and covering more than 7 square miles. Most of the depressions are much smaller. Only after heavy rains do these blowouts hold water. A thin crust of salt (halite) crystals, formed by the evaporation of water, typically coats the surfaces of the blowouts.

Puebloans used and traded the salt from the blowouts. When Spaniards arrived, they recognized the value of this salt for more than just flavoring and preserving food. In 1554, Bartolomé de Medina developed a method of refining silver ore known as the patio process, which required salt. Spaniards sent salt harvested from the blowouts 700 miles south to mines in Chihuahua, Mexico. Ruins of Spanish period pueblos can be seen at the nearby Salinas Pueblo Missions National Monument.

A blowout at Laguna del Perro with a pale surface of salt crystals.

115

iridium layer

IRIDIUM LAYER

A prominent sign marks the iridium layer in the Raton Formation.

Climax Canyon Park
THE DINOSAUR DEATH LAYER EXPOSED

From the Triassic to the Cretaceous Period (252 to 66 million years ago), dinosaurs roamed the Earth. Then, at the end of the Cretaceous, a 6-mile-wide asteroid struck the Earth near today's Yucatán Peninsula of Mexico. This collision ejected massive amounts of debris into the atmosphere that dramatically altered the climate and helped kill about 75 percent of all life on Earth. The debris, enriched in the rare element iridium from the meteorite, settled out of the atmosphere and marks the end of the Cretaceous and the extinction of the dinosaurs.

At the time of the meteorite impact, the Raton area was the swampy edge of the receding Western Interior Seaway.

Debris from the meteorite impact accumulated in the stagnant waters and on the deltas of sluggish rivers. The iridium-rich layer marking this important event, known to geologists as the Cretaceous/Tertiary boundary (K/T boundary), can be seen in Climax Canyon Park just outside Raton. A metal sign along the road indicates where to find the thin, pale-gray iridium-rich layer of clay. A similar layer has been found at sites around the world where sediment was actively accumulating at the end of Cretaceous time. The time boundary has been renamed the K/Pg boundary because the Tertiary Period was officially replaced with the Paleogene (Pg) and Neogene Periods.

To get to the park, take Moulton Avenue west from Raton. After about half a mile, turn left on Hill Street, which becomes Scenic Highway. Follow the winding road to a picnic area and a sign marking the iridium layer.

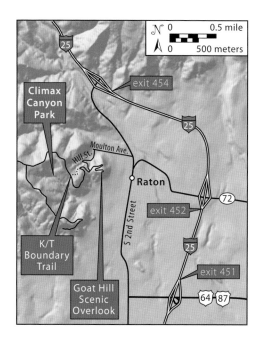

The iridium layer is a pale-gray, 4-inch-wide clay layer beneath dark organic shale and coal. The yellow field book is 7.5 inches long.

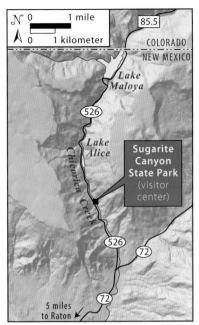

To get to Sugarite Canyon State Park, drive 5.5 miles east from Raton on NM 72 and then turn north on NM 526.

Sugarite Canyon State Park
53 COAL MINING IN NEW MEXICO

Just over 65 million years ago, the area of Sugarite Canyon was covered by the Western Interior Seaway that stretched across the central part of North America and separated the continent into two landmasses. The oldest rocks in the park are the late Cretaceous Pierre Shale that was deposited as mud on the bottom of this sea. This formation is known for its marine fossils, especially ammonites. As sea level dropped, barrier islands and river deltas covered the area, creating the light-colored Trinidad Sandstone. The trace fossil *Ophiomorpha*, the preserved burrow of a crustacean that lived in the coastal environment, is commonly found in the sandstone. As sea level dropped even more, coastal rivers, floodplains, and swamps developed, resulting in the formation of sandstone, mudstone, shale, and coal of the Raton Formation, which also preserves numerous plant fossils.

Rocks of the Raton Formation were deposited from the late Cretaceous into the early Paleogene Period. Included in this sedimentary package is the thin layer of debris that rained out of the atmosphere from the meteorite impact that helped cause the mass extinction of the dinosaurs and other organisms at the end of the Cretaceous. Unfortunately, this thin layer is not well exposed at Sugarite Canyon due to landslides. Better exposures can be found at Climax Canyon Park in Raton (site 52).

Much more recently, volcanic activity related to the Raton-Clayton volcanic field (see site 54) affected the area. Basaltic lava flows dated between 9 and 7 million years old form the caprock of the mesas surrounding the canyon.

Sugarite Canyon was an important source of coal and water to the people of Raton and the Santa Fe Railroad. Small-scale coal mining began in the canyon in the early 1900s, and by 1908 the Sugarite Coal Camp had been established. These mines operated until 1942. To supply both the city of Raton and the Santa Fe Railroad, a series of reservoirs—Lake Alice, Lake Maloya, and Lake Dorothy (in Colorado)—were created in the late 1800s to early 1900s. After the mines closed, many houses were moved or dismantled for materials, but you can still see foundations and waste piles from the mining activities in the canyon.

Waste rock from one of the coal mines drapes the side of Sugarite Canyon. The light rock in the background is sandstone.

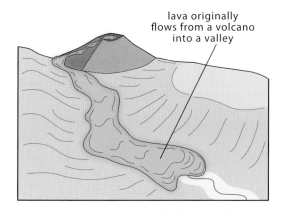

lava originally flows from a volcano into a valley

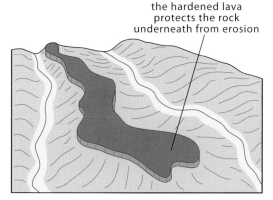

the hardened lava protects the rock underneath from erosion

Inverted topography developed in the Raton-Clayton volcanic field. Lava flowed into valleys and cooled. The hardened lava protected the softer sediments beneath it from erosion, but unprotected sediment wore away so that mesas now stand in the location of former valleys.

54 Capulin Volcano National Monument
LANDSCAPE OF THE RATON-CLAYTON VOLCANIC FIELD

Between Raton and Clayton, US 64 crosses a region of mesas capped with black basalt, small cinder cones, and larger shield volcanoes. This dramatic display of youthful volcanism is the Raton-Clayton volcanic field, which was active from 9 million years ago to as recently as 32,000 years ago. Eruptions occurred from more than one hundred vents. The best-known volcano in the area is Capulin, a cinder cone that erupted about 56,000 years ago when basalt with a high gas content rose to the surface. The gases provided the eruption with energy, so the lava exploded from the vent, piling up fragments into the 1,300-foot-high cinder cone. The eruption lasted anywhere from a few weeks to a few years. Following the cone-building phase, a series of lava flows erupted from a *boca*, a small vent at the base of the volcano. Around Capulin and its associated lava flows, you can see small mounds, called tumuli, that formed when slow-moving molten lava within a flow swelled and cracked the overlying crust. Also visible are spatter cones, lava tubes, and solidified lava lakes.

A winding road leads to the top of Capulin. Along the way, the layers of volcanic material that built the cinder cone are exposed. Once at the top, you can peer down into the volcano's crater. The summit of Capulin also provides an excellent view of

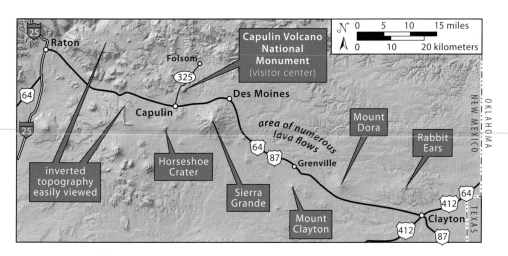

Many of the volcanic features of this area are easily viewed along US 87 between Clayton and Raton.

Basalt fragments were explosively erupted and piled up in layers around the volcanic vent to create the Capulin cinder cone.

A road winds around the Capulin cinder cone to its crater at the top. A boca, where lava flowed from the base of the cinder cone, appears as a small hill to the left of the cinder cone.

the flat basalt-capped mesas of the Raton-Clayton volcanic field. During eruptions, the fluid basalt lava flowed into low areas and along stream valleys and solidified. The hardened lava, which is resistant to erosion, protected the soft sediments under it. Over time, the rocks around the lava flow eroded, leaving the former valley as a tall mesa. This reversal in landscape is called inverted topography.

Sierra Grande, the large mountain south of Capulin, rises more than 2,000 feet above the surrounding plains. This 2.67-million-year-old volcano has the classic profile of a shield volcano with very gentle slopes. Unlike typical shield volcanoes that are composed of layers of basalt flows, Sierra Grande formed from andesite flows. It is also the only volcano in the Raton-Clayton volcanic field to erupt two-pyroxene andesite, meaning the lava contains both the minerals clinopyroxene and orthopyroxene.

Rabbit Ear Mountain, located north of Clayton, erupted about 3 million years ago. The mountain and a neighboring butte, together known as Rabbit Ears, were important landmarks for travelers following the Cimarron Route (or Dry Route) of the Santa Fe Trail because several reliable water sources were located near them.

The Sierra Grande shield volcano viewed from the top of Capulin.

Clayton Lake State Park
TRACKS ON THE DINOSAUR FREEWAY

In 1955, Clayton Lake was created for recreational fishing and as a wildlife refuge with the construction of an earthen dam across Seneca Creek. In 1982, the lake overflowed into the dam's spillway, eroding a few inches of sandstone and revealing more than five hundred dinosaur tracks in four distinct rock layers. The tracks are found in the approximately 100-million-year-old sedimentary rocks of the Dakota Sandstone that were deposited near the shoreline of the Western Interior Seaway. Dinosaurs walked across some of these muddy coastal areas, leaving their footprints behind. Although parallel trackways showing animals walking side by side are not obvious at Clayton Lake, they are found in Dakota Sandstone all the way to northern Colorado and indicate that groups of dinosaurs migrated along the coastal plain at the edge of the Western Interior Seaway. Many paleontologists call this the Dinosaur Freeway.

The most abundant tracks preserved belong to adult iguanodonts, but there are also tracks of a baby iguanodont, the large carnivore *Acrocanthosaurus*, and a crocodile. A possible trackway of a stegosaur has also been identified. Sometimes an animal slipped in the mud, as shown by a set of tracks that record where a dinosaur used its tail to steady itself. Another unique track shows where a dinosaur hesitated, shifting back and forth on its feet before deciding to walk forward, most likely warily checking the area for dangerous predators like *Acrocanthosaurus*. Other interesting geologic features at the site include plant fossils, worm burrows, and polygonal mud cracks that formed as muddy sediments dried.

Footprint of a plant-eating dinosaur. The yellow field book is 7.5 inches long.

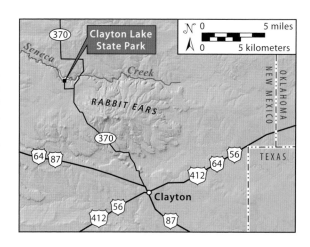

To get to Clayton Lake State Park, follow NM 370 north out of Clayton. After driving about 10.5 miles, turn left on NM 455 and follow it to the park.

Looking down on the trackway at Clayton Lake. The black impressions, filled with water, are footprints in the pale sandstone.

Blackwater Draw
HOME TO ICE-AGE HUNTERS

56

Blackwater Draw, a national historic landmark, is located on an arid, windswept grassland. During the last ice age, however, evergreen trees like pine, spruce, and fir thrived. The climate was wetter and milder, with frost-free winters and cooler summers. A spring-fed lake and marshland attracted many animals, including mammoths, bison, dire wolves, ground sloths, saber-toothed cats, peccaries, camels, horses, and turtles. The water source and animals also attracted a relatively new arrival to North America—humans.

An archaeological site was discovered here in 1929 by Ridgely Whiteman, an amateur archaeologist. A gravel-mining operation uncovered more ancient animal bones and stone spearpoints in 1931, drawing the attention of University of Pennsylvania archaeologist Edgar B. Howard, who began investigations the following year. This excavation yielded fluted stone tools that are unique to some of the earliest humans to occupy North America. Known as the Clovis Culture, these people used their finely crafted stone spearpoints to hunt ice-age mammals that roamed North America. An important food source was archaic bison, which were larger than modern bison and stood more than 7 feet at the shoulder with horns spreading 3 feet from tip to tip. Mammoth fossils with obvious signs of butchering show that these large elephant-like animals were also consumed. One of the most interesting discoveries at the site is a Clovis-aged hand-dug well, the oldest known human-made structure in North America.

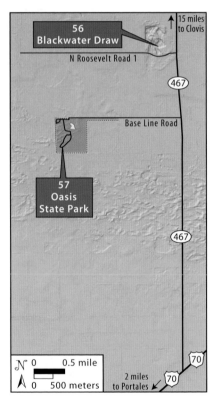

To get to Blackwater Draw, take NM 467 about 5 miles north from Portales.

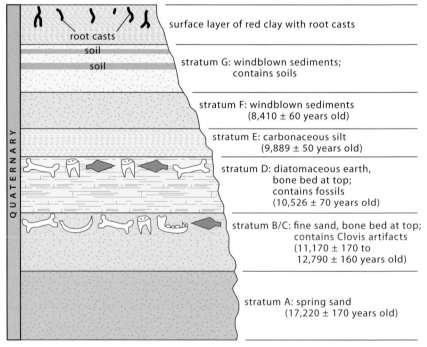

Stratigraphic section of Blackwater Draw showing the radiometric ages of different layers and the locations of preserved bone beds. Clovis artifacts are found in stratum B/C. Folsom artifacts have been excavated from stratum D.

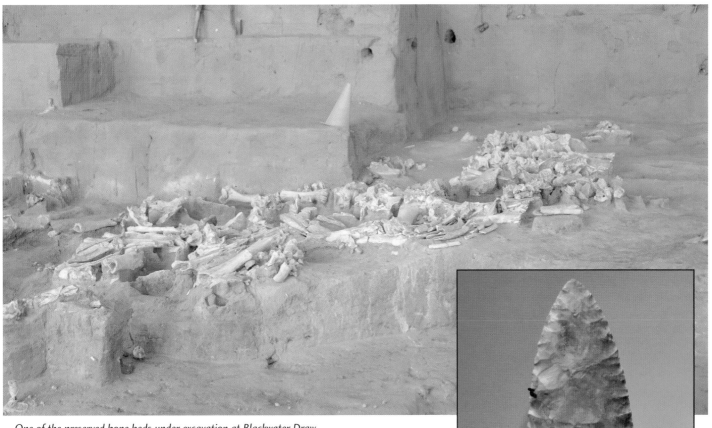

One of the preserved bone beds under excavation at Blackwater Draw.

Clovis people occupied Blackwater Draw for a few hundred years about 12,000 years ago. As the ice age ended, the climate of the region dried, vegetation changed, many large mammal species went extinct, and the Clovis Culture faded away. These people, however, did not become extinct. Recent genetic studies indicate that the Clovis people are the ancestors of many modern Native Americans. Later cultures, such as the Folsom people and Paleo-Indian groups, also inhabited Blackwater Draw.

Eastern New Mexico University, in Portales, currently owns the Blackwater Draw site and sponsors ongoing excavations. A winding trail with interpretive signs leads past the ancient pond and marsh deposits and the site of the Clovis-age hand-dug well. Visitors can also enter a building that protects the excavation site and view many of the preserved animal fossils. The university maintains a small museum on its campus in Portales that describes the history of Blackwater Draw and displays its numerous artifacts.

Clovis points were attached to the end of spears. This 4-inch-long specimen is on loan to the Houston Museum of Natural Science from Mr. William M. Wheless III.

The Llano Estacado and Oasis State Park
WATER ON THE STAKED PLAINS

The Llano Estacado, also called the Staked Plains, covers an area of about 32,000 square miles that extends from the Pecos River eastward to Palo Duro Canyon in Texas, and from the Canadian River southward to around Hobbs, New Mexico. This flat, featureless expanse, one of the largest tablelands in North America, developed on the Ogallala Formation. These stream, lake, and windblown sediments were eroded from the Rocky Mountains during the Miocene and Pliocene Epochs. Pale-white calcite, known as caliche, commonly cements the top of the Ogallala Formation into an erosion-resistant caprock that creates the tableland. In places, younger sedimentary rocks, such as the Blackwater Draw Formation, overlie the Ogallala Formation.

At Oasis State Park, the treeless expanse of the Llano Estacado is broken by a grove of cottonwood trees. Homesteader Will Taylor planted them in the early 1900s around an area of artesian springs. In this part of New Mexico, water in the Ogallala Formation is trapped between impermeable rocks of the underlying Chinle Group and the impermeable caprock. In places, the caprock is fractured, and in the past the groundwater rose to the surface. Settlements like Portales and Artesia, and many homesteads in the region, were located at springs.

Unfortunately, as the population grew and more groundwater was extracted for irrigation, the water table dropped, and now the springs no longer flow. It is unlikely that they will flow again because most of the water that's been taken from the Ogallala aquifer had been trapped there since the end of the Pleistocene Epoch. Recharge, the addition of water to the aquifer, is minute today compared to the amount withdrawn. Instead of the springs and small marshy areas that visitors would have seen in the late 1800s, numerous sand dunes now cover parts of the park. Agricultural activity, especially during the Dust Bowl, contributed to the establishment of the dunes. In 1973, an artificial lake, supplied with water from a well, was created at the park.

The origin of the name Llano Estacado, which roughly translates to "staked plain," is not known, although several possible explanations exist. Some speculate that the Comanche who lived in the area tied their horses to stakes in the ground to prevent them from running off. Another explanation describes early Spanish explorers driving stakes into the ground so they could find their way back out of the vast plains. A favored explanation is that *estacado*, which also translates to "palisade," refers to the caprock that looks like a palisade encircling the plains.

Today, an artificial lake at Oasis State Park is a popular local fishing hole stocked with catfish and trout.

Looking east from Mescalero Sands (site 59) at Mescalero Ridge, the edge of the Llano Estacado.

The Llano Estacado east of Roswell.

The Llano Estacado is a large, flat tableland spanning the border of New Mexico and Texas.

To visit Oasis State Park, take NM 467 north from Portales. Turn west on Base Line Road and follow it approximately 2 miles to the park.

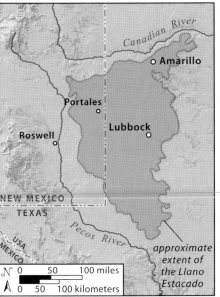

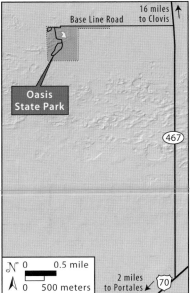

East of Roswell, at the edge of the Pecos River valley, is a series of nine small, round lakes. In the late 1800s, a group of cowboys tried to measure the depth of the lakes by tying a few ropes together and throwing the length into the water. When they were unable to make a measurement, they dubbed the lakes "bottomless." Modern measurements show the water depth to be around 90 feet in the deepest lake. Although not deep compared to large lakes, they are deep for their size because of an unusual geologic setting.

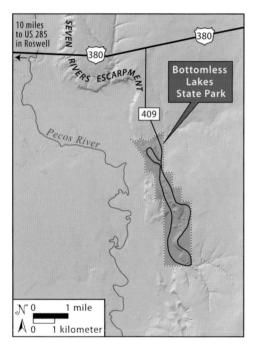

To get to Bottomless Lakes State Park, take US 380 about 10 miles east from Roswell. Turn south on County Road 409 (Bottomless Lakes Road) and follow it to the park.

In the Permian Period this area was at the edge of the Delaware Basin, an arm of a large, salty sea. Limestone and gypsum, as well as some sandstone and siltstone, were deposited in this sea, forming the rocks of the Seven Rivers Formation, which crop out in the park, and the underlying San Andres Limestone. Groundwater flowing through the San Andres Formation is part of a regional artesian aquifer that seeps upward under pressure toward the Seven Rivers Formation, slowly dissolving the soluble gypsum and creating cavities underground. Eventually, when the roof of a cavity cannot support its own weight, it collapses to form a sinkhole. The Bottomless Lakes are steep-sided sinkholes that extend below the water table, allowing groundwater to seep into the depressions and create permanent lakes. Sinkhole lakes such as these are termed *cenotes* in parts of Mexico, where they are common. Eight of the nine cenotes in the area are within the park boundary. Reliable water in an arid region is noteworthy, and Bottomless Lakes State Park was established in 1933, the oldest in New Mexico.

The Bottomless Lakes are located along the Seven Rivers escarpment, a steep slope that marks the eastern edge of the Pecos River floodplain. The base of this ridge is a long-abandoned channel of the river. The largest of the lakes, Lazy Lagoon, has an elongate shape because it occupies part of the ancient river channel. Back in the days when the cowboys first tried to measure the depth of the lakes, water overflowed from the cenotes to create an area of wetlands on the floodplain. Usage of groundwater for irrigation, however, caused a significant drop in the water table and ended overflow from the lakes.

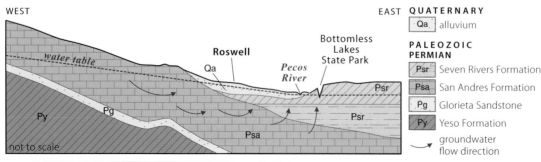

QUATERNARY

| Qa | alluvium |

PALEOZOIC
PERMIAN

Psr	Seven Rivers Formation
Psa	San Andres Formation
Pg	Glorieta Sandstone
Py	Yeso Formation

⌒ groundwater flow direction

Flow in the regional artesian aquifer seeps upward, dissolving the gypsum bedrock to create the cenotes in Bottomless Lakes State Park.

Distinctive light and dark layers in the gypsum of the Seven Rivers Formation are likely seasonal layers called varves. The lighter gypsum layers precipitated in the dry season during high evaporation rates. The darker layers usually contain more calcite and organic material that formed during a wetter season when fresh water reduced the salinity and allowed plankton to grow. This outcrop is located on the east side of Bottomless Lakes Road near Lazy Lagoon.

The sinkholes at Bottomless Lakes State Park have the steep sides and permanent water typical of a cenote.

59 Mescalero Sands
A MOSTLY STABILIZED DUNE FIELD

If you drive east from Roswell on US 380 toward the low escarpment at the western edge of the Llano Estacado, you'll begin to notice low, undulating hills of the Mescalero Sands on both sides of the road. This sand sheet formed in two distinct time periods from material eroded mostly from the Ogallala Formation, a major rock unit exposed throughout the region. The Lower Sand Sheet was deposited between 90,000 and 50,000 years ago. From around 50,000 to 18,000 years ago, the climate of the region was cooler and wetter, and an ancient soil, called the Berino paleosol, developed on top of the Lower Sand Sheet as the sand became hidden beneath a sagebrush grassland. The water table was higher than it is today, and many springs and wetlands, known in New Mexico as *ciénagas*, dotted the area. Fragments of horse and mammoth fossils, as well as abundant

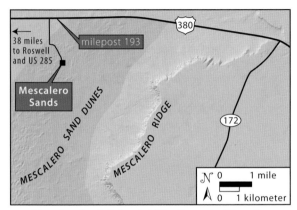

Mescalero Sands is located 38 miles east of Roswell on US 380. Watch for Bureau of Land Management signs announcing the Mescalero Sands Recreation Area.

Small ripples on the surface of the sand show that some of the dunes are active, and sand is accumulating around yuccas.

Looking east at landscape typical of Mescalero Sands.

fossil snails, are associated with the ancient wetlands. From 18,000 to 5,000 years ago, as the climate dried and the water table dropped, sand dunes were once again active, forming what is known as the Upper Sand Sheet that covered the grassland and paleosol.

For most of the past 5,000 years, these dunes have been again stabilized by vegetation. Since about 1880, however, disturbance of the landscape by cattle and agriculture has allowed some active sand to blow around and shift the dunes. Strong winds sometimes blow sand over the edge of the Llano Estacado, known here as Mescalero Ridge, and have created smaller dune fields. Sand also accumulates around the base of shrubs, usually mesquite, forming *nabkhas*, also known as coppice dunes. Crescent-shaped parabolic dunes are more common in areas where shinnery oak grows. Where vegetation is absent, transverse dunes form.

About 265 to 260 million years ago, during the Permian Period, the southeastern portion of New Mexico was at the edge of a large, shallow sea. Diverse organisms, including sponges, algae, crinoids, bryozoans, and rugose corals lived in this sea and built an imposing reef. Known as the Capitan Reef, it can be seen at the surface in Guadalupe Mountains National Park in Texas. In New Mexico you can explore a cave in these reef rocks at Carlsbad Caverns.

Most caves form as groundwater, slightly acidic due to the presence of small amounts of carbonic acid, dissolves limestone and dolomite. Carbonic acid forms when atmospheric carbon dioxide is dissolved in water. Carlsbad Caverns and other surrounding caves formed in a different, unique way. About 6 to 4 million years ago, hydrogen sulfide from oil and natural gas seeped upward from deep underground. When this gas encountered oxygenated groundwater, it became sulfuric acid, which dissolved away rocks of the ancient reef and created a vast network of caves that includes well over 100 miles of mapped passages.

Carlsbad Caverns is known for its abundant and diverse speleothems, or cave formations. Beginning about 1 million years ago, as the water table dropped and the cave dried, water began percolating down from the surface, carrying the mineral calcite in solution and depositing it as the water entered the cave. The type of cave formation created depends on the behavior of water in the cave. Dripping water creates stalactites and stalagmites that can form a column or pillar when joined. Water flowing over a surface forms flowstone. Helictites, curved and contorted twists of calcite that grow sideways out of the cave walls, are thought to occur where water seeps to the surface of the rock

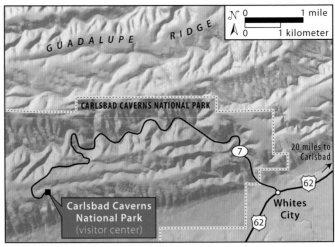

The entrance to Carlsbad Caverns National Park is located on US 62 about 20 miles south of Carlsbad.

Speleothems in Carlsbad are usually white or pale gray, but elements such as iron and manganese leached from bedrock and soil can add color, as seen here in Devils Spring. —Photograph by Peter Jones, National Park Service

and evaporates, although the exact mechanism of formation is not completely understood. Where water pools in caves, drops of mineral-rich water can land on the pool surface and spread out, creating thin films of calcite floating on the water. Cave rims form due to the condensation of water that occurs as warm, humid air hits a cold rock surface. Various combinations of these processes create additional speleothems, such as cave pearls, drapery, and cave popcorn. Most of Carlsbad's speleothems were created during the last ice age, when the climate of New Mexico was wetter and more water seeped into the ground. With today's arid climate, the creation of new speleothems is limited.

Speleothems in Carlsbad Caverns take many beautiful and unique shapes.
—Photograph by Larry Maltby

A winding pathway leads into the natural entrance of Carlsbad Caverns.
—Photograph by Peter Jones, National Park Service

GLOSSARY

aa. Hawaiian term for lava with a jagged, blocky surface.

amphibolite. A metamorphic rock containing amphibole and plagioclase with little to no quartz. It typically forms during regional metamorphism under moderate to high temperature and pressure.

andesite. Fine-grained volcanic rock, typically medium gray in color, containing plagioclase and a combination of the minerals augite, orthopyroxene, and hornblende.

anticline. An upward-arched fold with the oldest rocks in the center.

aquifer. A body of rock or sediment with good porosity and permeability that holds and readily transmits groundwater.

ash. Pyroclastic material that is smaller than 2 millimeters in diameter.

ash-flow tuff. The rock formed from the consolidation and compaction of an ash-flow deposit.

asthenosphere. The zone of somewhat malleable rock beneath the lithosphere. It is the zone over which the lithospheric plates move.

basalt. Fine-grained, typically dark-colored volcanic rock containing plagioclase and pyroxene.

basement. Crystalline igneous and metamorphic rocks that are overlain by younger sedimentary rock layers.

bedding. The layering as seen in a sedimentary rock. A single layer is called a **bed**. When different rock types are interlayered with each other, they are described as **interbedded**.

blowout. A depression caused by the removal of sand, silt, and clay by wind.

boca. A small vent at the base of an active volcano from which lava erupts.

brachiopod. A marine invertebrate characterized by two bilaterally symmetrical shells. It lived from the Cambrian to today.

breccia. A rock consisting of angular fragments.

bryozoan. An invertebrate characterized by branching sticklike colonial growth. It lived from the Ordovician to today.

caldera. A large volcanic depression formed after a large eruption as land collapses into the emptied magma chamber below.

cenote. A steep-sided sinkhole that reaches down below the water table.

cinder cone. A conical hill composed of pyroclastics (usually basalt or andesite in composition) that accumulated around a volcanic vent.

cirque. A steep-sided, bowl-shaped depression at the head of a valley or on a mountainside formed by glacial erosion.

coarse grained. A term used to describe a rock with large particles or crystals about 1 millimeter in diameter or larger and typically visible to the naked eye.

columnar jointing. The fracturing in a lava flow that causes the flow to break into columns.

conglomerate. A sedimentary rock composed of particles that exceed 2 millimeters in diameter.

crinoid. An echinoderm with a cup-shaped body, numerous feathery arms, and a stalk for attachment to the seafloor. This animal lived from the Ordovician to today.

cross bedding. A layering in sedimentary rock that forms at an angle to horizontal.

crust. The uppermost layer of Earth. Continental crust consists mainly of an igneous and/or metamorphic basement overlain by sedimentary and volcanic rock. Oceanic crust consists of basalt and gabbro.

dacite. A fine-grained, typically light-colored volcanic rock similar to andesite but containing quartz.

debris flow. A chaotic water-laden mixture of differently sized material that flows rapidly downward in response to gravity; also called a mudslide.

diatreme. A carrot-shaped, breccia-filled volcanic conduit formed in an explosive eruption.

dike. A tabular body of intrusive igneous rock that cuts across the surrounding country rock.

erosion. The movement or transport of weathered material by water, ice, wind, or gravity.

fault. A fracture or zone of fractures in Earth's crust along which blocks of rock on either side have shifted.

fault block. A piece of crust bounded by faults.

feldspar. The most abundant rock-forming mineral group. Makes up 60 percent of Earth's crust and contains calcium, sodium, or potassium with aluminum silicate. Includes plagioclase feldspars and alkali feldspars.

felsic. An adjective describing light-colored igneous rocks containing abundant quartz, feldspar, and muscovite.

fine grained. A term used to describe a rock with small particles or crystals less than about 1 millimeter in diameter and typically not visible to the naked eye.

fissure. An open crack.

floodplain. The portion of a river valley adjacent to the river that is built of sediments deposited when the river overflows its banks during flooding.

formation. A body of sedimentary, igneous, or metamorphic rock that can be recognized over a large area. It is the basic stratigraphic unit in geologic mapping. A formation may be part of a larger group and may be broken into members.

fossils. The remains, imprints, or traces of plants or animals preserved in rock.

geode. A hollow area in a rock lined with mineral crystals.

gneiss. A coarse-grained, metamorphic rock formed during high-grade regional metamorphism and characterized by light and dark bands of minerals.

granite. A coarse-grained intrusive igneous rock consisting of quartz, alkali feldspar, and mica.

granodiorite. A coarse-grained intrusive igneous rock consisting of quartz, plagioclase, alkali feldspar, and hornblende.

group. Two or more formations that occur together.

gypsum. Hydrous calcium sulphate ($CaSO_4 \cdot 2H_2O$), a soluble mineral that forms as water evaporates.

hoodoo. A uniquely shaped column, pillar, or spire of rock shaped by differential weathering.

ignimbrite. A volcanic rock consisting of ash and pumice deposited by a pyroclastic flow.

intrusive igneous rocks. Rocks that cool from magma beneath the surface of Earth. The body of rock is called an **intrusion**.

island arc. An offshore volcanic arc or linear chain of volcanoes formed along a convergent plate margin.

joint. A fracture in a rock without displacement.

kipuka. A Hawaiian term for land completely surrounded and isolated by a lava flow.

lava. Molten rock erupted on the surface of Earth.

limestone. A sedimentary rock composed of calcium carbonate formed by precipitation in warm water, usually aided by biological activity.

lineament. A regional linear feature believed to reflect crustal structure.

lithosphere. The outer rigid shell of Earth that is broken into tectonic plates. On average, continental lithosphere is about 100 miles thick and old oceanic lithosphere is about 60 miles thick.

maar. A volcanic crater produced in an explosive eruption, often from the interaction of magma and groundwater.

magma. Molten rock within Earth.

mantle. The part of Earth between the interior core and the outer crust.

metamorphic rock. A rock derived from preexisting rock that has changed mineralogically or texturally, or both, in response to changes in temperature and/or pressure, usually deep within Earth. A rock that undergoes these changes is said to be **metamorphosed**.

minette. An uncommon igneous rock composed of biotite and orthoclase.

moraine. A pile of sediment that was carried and deposited by a glacier.

mudstone. A sedimentary rock composed of mud.

normal fault. A fault created by tensional stress in which the overlying block of rock moves down relative to the underlying block of rock.

obsidian. A dark-colored volcanic glass.

ore. A rock that contains desirable minerals in concentrations that are economic to extract.

orogeny. A mountain building event.

pahoehoe. A Hawaiian term for lava with a ropy, corded surface.

paleosol. An ancient soil.

pegmatite. A very coarse-grained, usually granitic, igneous rock with crystals at least 2.5 centimeters long.

petroglyph. A carving on a rock.

plagioclase. A feldspar mineral rich in sodium and calcium. One of the most common rock-forming minerals in igneous and metamorphic rocks.

Pleistocene. The last 2.6 million years of geologic time, during which periods of extensive continental glaciation alternated with warmer interglacial periods of glacial retreat.

pumice. A very porous volcanic rock formed in an explosive eruption when a gas-rich lava solidifies rapidly.

pyroclastic. Fragments of rock violently ejected from a volcano.

pyroclastic flow. A very hot, rapidly moving mix of lava, pumice, ash, and volcanic gas erupted from a volcano.

quartz. A mineral composed entirely of silica; one of the most common rock-forming minerals.

regression. A fall in global sea level.

rhyolite. A fine-grained volcanic rock that is typically pale gray to pink in color and contains quartz, sanidine, plagioclase, and minor amounts of hornblende and biotite.

rift. A linear valley marking where a tectonic plate is being pulled apart, or was pulled apart in the past, by tensional tectonic forces.

salina. An isolated body of saline water.

sandstone. A sedimentary rock made primarily of sand.

schist. A metamorphic rock that is strongly layered due to an abundance of visible, platy minerals.

sedimentary rock. A rock formed from the compaction and cementation of sediment.

shield volcano. A low, wide volcano created by very fluid lava flows.

sill. A tabular body of intrusive igneous rock that is parallel to sedimentary layers in the surrounding rock.

siltstone. A sedimentary rock made primarily of silt.

spatter cone. A very small, cone-shaped structure on a lava flow formed as blobs of lava are thrown a few feet into the air and land while still molten.

speleothem. Any structure formed in a cave by the deposition of minerals from water.

stock. An irregularly shaped body of intrusive igneous rock with less than 100 square kilometers exposed at Earth's surface.

stratovolcano. A tall, cone-shaped volcano composed of layers of lava flows and pyroclastic deposits usually composed of andesite, dacite, or rhyolite.

subduction. The process of an oceanic plate sinking into the asthenosphere under another tectonic plate.

supergene enrichment. A near-surface process in which oxidation produces acidic groundwater that leaches metals, carries them downward, and precipitates them to enrich the primary ore already present.

suture zone. The joining together of terranes along a major fault zone.

syenite. A coarse-grained intrusive igneous rock consisting of orthoclase feldspar, lesser to minor amounts of plagioclase feldspar, minor amounts of augite and hornblende, and no quartz.

talus. A pile of rocks that accumulates at the base of a cliff from falling rocks.

tarn. A rock-basin lake formed in a cirque.

tectonic. Referring to large-scale processes affecting the structure of the Earth's crust.

terrane. A block of crust with a unique geologic history.

thunderegg. A solid or near-solid nodule formed by magmatic and volcanic processes and found only in volcanic rocks.

trachybasalt. A fine-grained volcanic rock containing alkali feldspar, calcic plagioclase, olivine, clinopyroxene.

transgression. A rise in global sea level.

travertine. A deposit of calcium carbonate ($CaCO_3$) formed by a spring or in caves.

tuff. An igneous rock composed of ash, pumice, and other debris erupted explosively from a volcano.

tumulus (plural = tumuli). An elliptical, domed structure in a pahoehoe flow formed when slow-moving molten lava within the flow swells or pushes the overlying crust upward.

unconformity. A surface between two rock units representing a gap in geologic time.

varve. An annual sedimentary deposit usually consisting of two distinctive seasonal layers.

vein. A tabular body of minerals precipitated in cracks in rock.

vent. The actual place where volcanic materials erupt. Vents are either eruptive localities on large volcanoes or mark much smaller volcanoes.

volcanic bomb. Molten lava greater than 64 millimeters in diameter that is ejected in a molten state from a volcano and is shaped into an aerodynamic, teardrop form as it flies through the air and cools.

volcanic dome. A mound-shaped landform created by an eruption of viscous lava that cannot flow far from its vent.

volcanic neck. The eroded remnant of solidified lava filling the conduit of an extinct volcano.

weathering. The physical disintegration and chemical decomposition of rock at Earth's surface.

xenolith. A foreign rock contained within an igneous rock.

zeolite. Aluminum-silicate minerals, containing sodium, potassium, or calcium, that commonly form where volcanic rocks or ash interact with groundwater or volcanic fluids.

FURTHER READING

Allen, J. E., and F. E. Kottlowski. 1958. *Roswell–Ruidoso–Valley of Fires, Including Trips to Lincoln, Tularosa, and Bottomless Lakes State Park,* 3rd Edition. New Mexico Bureau of Geology and Mineral Resources Scenic Trips to the Geologic Past 3.

Baltz, E. H., and D. A. Myers. 1999. *Stratigraphic Framework of Upper Paleozoic Rocks, Southeastern Sangre de Cristo Mountains, New Mexico.* New Mexico Bureau of Geology and Mineral Resources Memoir 48.

Bauer, P. W., J. C. Love, J. H. Schilling, and J. E. Taggart, Jr. 1991. *The Enchanted Circle: Loop Drives from Taos,* 5th Edition. New Mexico Bureau of Geology and Mineral Resources Scenic Trips to the Geologic Past 2.

Beus, S. S., ed. 1987. *Rocky Mountain Section of the Geological Society of America: Centennial Field Guide 2.* Boulder, Colorado: Geological Society of America.

Cather, S. M., and C. E. Chapin. 1989. Day 2: Field guide to upper Eocene and lower Oligocene volcaniclastic rocks of the northern Mogollon-Datil volcanic field. In *Field Excursions to Volcanic Terranes in the Western United States, Volume I. Southern Rocky Mountain Region,* eds. C. E. Chapin and J. Zidek, New Mexico Bureau of Geology and Mineral Resources Memoir 46, p. 60–68.

Chamberlin, R. M., B. S. Kues, S. M. Cather, J. M. Barker, and W. C. McIntosh, eds. 1994. *Mogollon Slope, West-Central New Mexico.* New Mexico Geological Society Fall Field Conference 45.

Chamberlin, R. M., V. T. McLemore, M. R. Bowie, and J. L. Post. 1987. Roadlog from Socorro to Blue Canyon area of Socorro Peak, to US-60 clay pit, and to Luis Lopez manganese district. In *Guidebook for the 1987 Conference,* 24th Annual Meeting of the Clay Minerals Society and 36th Annual Clay Minerals Conference, compilers V. T. McLemore and M. R. Bowie, New Mexico Bureau of Geology and Mineral Resources, p. 15–21.

Chapin, C. E., and J. F. Callender, eds. 1983. *Socorro Region II.* New Mexico Geological Society Fall Field Conference 34.

Chapin, C. E., W. E. Elston, and H. L. James, eds. 1978. *Field Guide to Selected Cauldrons and Mining Districts of the Datil-Mogollon Volcanic Field, New Mexico.* New Mexico Geological Society Special Publication 7.

Chapin, C. E., and J. Zidek. 1989. *Field Excursions to Volcanic Terranes in the Western United States,* Volume I. Southern Rocky Mountain Region: New Mexico Bureau of Geology and Mineral Resources Memoir 46.

Clemons, R. E. 1996. *A Trip through Space and Time: Las Cruces to Cloudcroft.* New Mexico Bureau of Geology and Mineral Resources Scenic Trips to the Geologic Past 15.

Clemons, R. E., W. E. King, G. H. Mack, and J. Zidek, eds. 1986. *Truth or Consequences Region.* New Mexico Geological Society Fall Field Conference Guidebook 37.

Disbrow, A. E., and W. C. Stoll. 1957. *Geology of the Cerrillos Area, Santa Fe County, New Mexico.* New Mexico Bureau of Geology and Mineral Resources Bulletin 48.

Dunbar, N. W. 1999. Cosmogenic ^{36}Cl-determined age of the Carrizozo lava flows, south-central New Mexico. *New Mexico Geology* 21 (2): 26–29.

Dunbar, N., S. Lucas, M. Zimmerer, and A. Jochems. 2019. Organ Mountains–Desert Peaks and Prehistoric Trackways National Monuments. *Lite Geology* 44: 3–5.

Eveleth, R. W., and G. R. Osburn. 1985. The Kneeling Nun, Santa Rita, New Mexico. *New Mexico Geology* 7 (3): 56–58.

Ferguson, H. G. 1927. *Geology and Ore Deposits of the Mogollon Mining District, New Mexico.* US Geological Survey Bulletin 787.

Goff, F., B. S. Kues, M. A. Rogers, L. S. McFadden, and J. N. Gardner, eds. 1996. *Jemez Mountains Region.* New Mexico Geological Society Fall Field Conference 47.

Goff, F., and L. Shevenell. 1987. Travertine deposits of Soda Dam, New Mexico, and their implications for the age and evolution of the Valles caldera hydrothermal system. *GSA Bulletin* 99 (2): 292–302.

Hallett, R. B. 1992. Volcanic geology of the Rio Puerco necks. In *San Juan Basin IV,* eds. S. G. Lucas, B. S. Kues, T. E. Williamson, and A. P. Hunt, New Mexico Geological Society Fall Field Conference 43, p. 135–44.

Harley, G. T. 1934. *The Geology and Ore Deposits of Sierra County, New Mexico.* New Mexico Bureau of Geology and Mineral Resources Bulletin 10.

Hill, C. A. 1987. *Geology of Carlsbad Cavern and Other Caves in the Guadalupe Mountains, New Mexico and Texas.* New Mexico Bureau of Geology and Mineral Resources Bulletin 117.

Jicha, H. L. 1954. *Geology and Mineral Deposits of Lake Valley Quadrangle, Grant, Luna, and Sierra Counties, New Mexico.* New Mexico Bureau of Geology and Mineral Resources Bulletin 37.

KellerLynn, K. 2012. *El Malpais National Monument Geologic Resources Inventory Report*. Fort Collins, Colorado, National Park Service, Natural Resource Report NPS/NRSS/GRD/NRR—2012/578.

KellerLynn, K. 2014. *El Morro National Monument Geologic Resources Inventory Report*. Fort Collins, Colorado, National Park Service, Natural Resource Report NPS/NRSS/GRD/NRR—2012/588.

KellerLynn, K. 2014. *Gila Cliff Dwellings National Monument Geologic Resources Inventory Report*. Fort Collins, Colorado, National Park Service, Natural Resource Report NPS/NRSS/GRD/NRR—2014/849.

KellerLynn, K. 2015. *Bandelier National Monument Geologic Resources Inventory Report*. Fort Collins, Colorado, National Park Service, Natural Resource Report NPS/NRSS/GRD/NRR—2015/1036.

KellerLynn, K. 2015. *Capulin Volcano National Monument Geologic Resources Inventory Report*. Fort Collins, Colorado, National Park Service, Natural Resource Report NPS/NRSS/GRD/NRR—2015/1031.

KellerLynn, K. 2015. *Chaco Culture National Historical Park Geologic Resources Inventory Report*. Fort Collins, Colorado, National Park Service, Natural Resource Report NPS/NRSS/GRD/NRR—2015/1045.

KellerLynn, K. 2017. *Petroglyph National Monument Geologic Resources Inventory Report*. Fort Collins, Colorado, National Park Service, Natural Resource Report NPS/NRSS/GRD/NRR— 2017/1547.

Kelley, V. C., and S. A. Northrop. 1975. *Geology of Sandia Mountains and Vicinity, New Mexico*. New Mexico Bureau of Geology and Mineral Resources Memoir 29.

Land, L. A. 2003. Evaporite karst and regional ground-water circulation in the lower Pecos valley of southeastern New Mexico. *Oklahoma Geological Survey Circular* 109: 227–32.

Land, L., V. W. Lueth, W. Raatz, P. Boston, and D. L. Love, eds. 2006. *Caves and Karst of Southeastern New Mexico*. New Mexico Geological Society Fall Field Conference Guidebook 57.

Lasky, S. G. 1932. *The Ore Deposits of Socorro County, New Mexico*. New Mexico Bureau of Geology and Mineral Resources Bulletin 8.

Loughlin, G. F., and A. H. Koschmann. 1942. *Geology and Ore Deposits of the Magdalena Mining District, New Mexico*. US Geological Survey Professional Paper 200.

Lozinsky, R. P., R. W. Harrison, and S. H. Lekson. 1995. *Elephant Butte Eastern Black Range Region: Journeys from Desert Lakes to Mountain Ghost Towns*. New Mexico Bureau of Geology and Mineral Resources Scenic Trips to the Geologic Past 16.

Lucas, S. G., and S. G. Dalman. 2016. The early Cretaceous Clayton Lake dinosaur tracksite, northeastern New Mexico. In *Fossil Record 5*, eds. R. M. Sullivan and S. G. Lucas, *New Mexico Museum of Natural History and Science Bulletin* 74: 127–40.

Lucas, S. G., and A. P. Hunt, eds. 1987. *Northeastern New Mexico*. New Mexico Geological Society Fall Field Conference Guidebook 38.

Lucas, S. G., G. S. Morgan, and K. E. Zeigler, eds. 2005. *New Mexico's Ice Ages*. New Mexico Museum of Natural History and Science Bulletin 28.

Lucas, S. G., and D. S. Ulmer-Scholle, eds. 2001. *Geology of the Llano Estacado*. New Mexico Geological Society Fall Field Conference Guidebook 52.

Lucas, S. G., S. Voigt, A. J. Lerner, J. P. MacDonald, J. A. Spielmann, and M. D. Celeskey. 2011. The Prehistoric Trackways National Monument, Permian of southern New Mexico, USA. *Ichnology Newsletter* 28: 10–14.

Lucas, S. G., K. E. Zeigler, V. W. Lueth, and D. E. Owen, eds. 2005. *Geology of the Chama Basin*. New Mexico Geological Society Fall Field Conference 56.

Mack, G., J. Witcher, and V. W. Lueth. 2008. *Geology of the Gila Wilderness–Silver City Area*. New Mexico Geological Society Fall Field Conference Guidebook 59.

Maldonado, F., and S. A. Kelley. 2009. Revisions to the stratigraphic nomenclature of the Abiquiu Formation, Abiquiu and contiguous areas, north-central New Mexico. *New Mexico Geology* 31: 3–8.

McLemore, V. T. 2017. *Mining Districts and Prospect Areas in New Mexico*. New Mexico Bureau of Geology and Mineral Resources.

McLemore, V. T. 2018. A geology guide to Red Rock Park. *Lite Geology* 43: 4.

Mueller, J. E., and C. R. Twidale. 1988. Geomorphic development of City of Rocks, Grant County, New Mexico. *New Mexico Geology* 10: 73–79.

Price, L. G., ed. 2010. *The Geology of Northern New Mexico's Parks, Monuments, and Public Lands*. New Mexico Bureau of Geology and Mineral Resources.

Rawling, G., V. T. McLemore, S. Timmons, and N. Dunbar, eds. 2014. *Geology of the Sacramento Mountains Region*. New Mexico Geological Society Fall Field Conference 65.

Seager, W. R. 1981. *Geology of Organ Mountains and Southern San Andres Mountains, New Mexico*. New Mexico Bureau of Geology and Mineral Resources Memoir 36.

Siemers, C. T., L. A. Woodward, and J. F. Callender, eds. 1974. *Ghost Ranch*. New Mexico Geological Society Fall Field Conference 25.

Titus, F. B. 1973. *Hydrogeologic Evolution of Estancia Valley: A Closed Basin in Central New Mexico*. New Mexico Bureau of Geology and Mineral Resources Open-File Report 69.

INDEX

WEB RESOURCES

Geology of New Mexico https://geoinfo.nmt.edu/tour/home.html

Mines and mineral localities of New Mexico https://www.mindat.org/loc-3991.html

Site 1: Ghost Ranch https://www.ghostranch.org/explore/the-land/

Site 3: Bisti/De-Na-Zin Wilderness https://www.blm.gov/visit/bisti-de-na-zin-wilderness

Site 4: Chaco Canyon https://www.nps.gov/chcu/learn/nature/geology.htm

Site 5: Cabezon Peak https://www.blm.gov/sites/blm.gov/files/NM_Cabezon_2018_508.pdf

Site 6: Red Rock Park https://geoinfo.nmt.edu/tour/state/red_rock/home.html

Site 7: El Morro https://www.nps.gov/elmo/learn/nature/geologicformations.htm

Site 8: Zuni Ice Cave and Bandera Crater https://www.icecaves.com/#home-section

Site 10: El Malpais National Monument https://www.nps.gov/elma/index.htm

Site 11: Mt. Taylor http://www.nmnaturalhistory.org/volcanoes/mt-taylor-volcanic-field

Site 14: Wheeler Peak https://www.fs.usda.gov/detail/carson/recreation/?cid=stelprdb5350403

Site 15: Harding Pegmatite http://eps.unm.edu/research/harding/index.html

Site 17: Valles Caldera https://volcanoes.usgs.gov/volcanoes/valles_caldera/

Site 18: Battleship Rock https://www.fs.usda.gov/detail/r3/landmanagement/resourcemanagement/?cid=stelprdb5195083

Site 19: Soda Dam https://www.fs.usda.gov/detail/r3/landmanagement/resourcemanagement/?cid=stelprdb5195088

Site 20: Kasha-Katuwe Tent Rocks National Monument https://www.blm.gov/programs/national-conservation-lands/new-mexico/kasha-katuwe-tent-rocks-national-monument

Site 22: Bandelier National Monument https://www.nps.gov/band/index.htm

Site 23: White Mesa and the Tierra Amarilla Anticline https://www.blm.gov/programs/recreation/mountainbike/whiteridge

Site 24: Cerrillos Hills State Park http://www.emnrd.state.nm.us/SPD/cerrilloshillsstatepark.html

Site 26: Petroglyph National Monument https://www.nps.gov/petr/index.htm

Site 27: San Lorenzo Canyon https://www.blm.gov/visit/san-lorenzo-canyon

Site 28: New Mexico Institute of Mining and Technology https://geoinfo.nmt.edu/museum/

Site 30: Quebradas Backcountry Byway https://geoinfo.nmt.edu/publications/guides/quebradas/home.html

Site 31: Trinity Site https://www.wsmr.army.mil/Trinity/Pages/Home.aspx

Site 35: Three Rivers Petroglyphs https://www.blm.gov/visit/three-rivers-petroglyph-site

Site 36: White Sands National Park https://www.nps.gov/whsa/learn/geology-of-white-sands.htm

Site 37: Dripping Springs Natural Area in the Organ Mountains https://www.blm.gov/visit/dripping-springs-natural-area

Site 38: Prehistoric Trackways National Monument https://www.blm.gov/visit/ptnm

Site 39: Kilbourne Hole https://www.blm.gov/visit/kilbourne-hole-volcanic-crater

Site 40: Sawtooth Mountains https://geoinfo.nmt.edu/tour/landmarks/monument_rock/home.html

Site 43: Chloride https://www.sierracountynewmexico.info/attractions/chloride-new-mexico/

Site 45: The Catwalk in Whitewater Canyon https://www.fs.usda.gov/recarea/gila/recarea/?recid=2029

Site 46: Gila Cliff Dwellings National Monument https://www.nps.gov/gicl/index.htm

Site 49: Lake Valley https://www.blm.gov/visit/lake-valley-historic-townsite

Site 54: Capulin Volcano National Monument https://www.nps.gov/cavo/index.htm

Site 56: Blackwater Draw https://www.enmu.edu/about/general-information/local-events-and-info/arts-and-culture/blackwater-draw-museum

Site 59: Mescalero Sands https://www.blm.gov/visit/mescalero-sands-north-dune-ohv-area

Site 60: Carlsbad Caverns National Park https://www.nps.gov/cave/index.htm

ABOUT THE AUTHOR AND PHOTOGRAPHER

NATHALIE BRANDES grew up studying geology with her father. She earned her BS and MS in geology at the New Mexico Institute of Mining and Technology (New Mexico Tech) and continued graduate studies at Michigan Technological University. She worked at the New Mexico Bureau of Geology and Mineral Resources; taught various geology courses at Michigan Tech, the University of Wisconsin–Eau Claire, and the University of Nevada—Las Vegas; and currently is a professor of geosciences at a community college.

PAUL BRANDES earned a BS in geology at the New Mexico Institute of Mining and Technology and an MS in geology at Michigan Technological University. He has worked as a geology consultant, an environmental enforcement officer, an exploration geologist, and a professor of geology at a community college. He has contributed photographs to several textbooks and laboratory manuals in geology and is on the management team of mindat.org.